Due

LOVE IN MARRIAGE

Love in marriage

The meaning and practice of sexual love in Christian Marriage

by Doctor Henri Gibert

With an Introduction by
Msgr. George A. Kelly
of The Family Life Bureau
Archdiocese of New York

Translated from the French by
ANDRÉ HUMBERT

HAWTHORN BOOKS, Inc. *Publishers* New York and London

First Edition, May, 1964

NIHIL OBSTAT

John A. Goodwine, S.T.L., J.C.D.
Censor Librorum

IMPRIMATUR

✠ Francis Cardinal Spellman
Archbishop of New York

H-5425

Table of Contents

PART TWO

The Physical Aspects of Love

Introduction

There is a sexual revolution going on all over the Western world. Even the most detached observer recognizes that values and institutions which are the result of Christian effort through two thousand years are now endangered. At stake are such things as the stability of marriage, the large family, conjugal chastity, pre-marital virginity, the role of wife and mother in family society, public laws governing contraception, sterilization, abortion, and child care.

Countless people have never accepted the Christian view of sex. Even many who did find that the high standards set by Christ and the Church for their sexual behavior were beyond them. Certainly down through the ages sins against the Sixth Commandment have been the most frequent matter of Confession. However, in spite of this, the Church has consistently worked to elevate man to Christ's view of sexuality and to inculcate through education and law those habits of life which make chaste living a desirable goal among men who are weak. Sometimes there were condemnations, as of adultery in the first four centuries and of contraception now, but more often it was day-in and day-out preaching and the extension of sacramental life which contributed to mankind's improved moral habits. By any perusal of history which allows comparison with the non-Christian world, the value of Christian doctrine on marriage and virginity is clearly seen. Granting the sins of Christians, for which Christ arranged a suitable remedy, Western nations, more than others, have succeeded in developing a strong monogamous family life, in exercising considerable control over male sexual appetites, in elevating women to the dignity of man's equal in the sexual relationship, in enhancing the education of children, and above all in fostering that kind of family life which might well be described as an eighth wonder of the world.

Not that such growth in Christian family virtues came at an even pace or without some confrontation, even inside the Church, with heresy and error. The Manicheans of the fourth century, the Catholic Jansenists of the eighteenth and the Protestant Puritans of the nineteenth all taught that the sexual experience was evil (some Protestants believed that the original sin of Adam and Eve was sexual), that at best it could be enjoyed only if babies were the natural outcome or intention, and that really sexual pleasure was the prerogative of husbands but not of wives. Such thinking led to repressive measures against sexual aberrations and public laws covering a variety of sexual acts, some of them even of a private nature.

In part the revolution of the twentieth century can be explained as a violent reaction, in and out of the Church, to some of the obvious distortions of the Victorian Era. History flows in ebbs and tides and Christian man does not long tolerate excesses such as were naturally the result of a dark view of human nature or of marriage (e.g. the frigid woman, uncontrolled biological fertility, neuroticism and psychosis created by bad parental training in these matters, etc., etc.)

But the twentieth century brought one even more radical innovation, the widespread use of contraception. Earlier peoples had tried to overcome the effects of over-fertility by homemade remedies, when it could not be accomplished by self-restraint or late marriages. The crudest contraceptives were first used by prostitutes. Only since World War I has contraception become a refined science. The impact of this new development was not immediately evident. Artificial birth control, recommended mostly for the alleviation of medical problems attendant on maternity, was offered as an answer to some acute personal problems for a minority of married women, not as a way of life for the majority. And whatever complaints sound religious thinkers had against some of the narrow-minded views of Victorians, all faiths, Catholic, Protestant, and Jewish condemned contraception as an unnatural practice in marriage and offensive to God's law on the use of marriage.

During the period between World I and II dynamic changes went on in family life and in culturally approved methods of birth control. Once it was felt that no inexorable connection need be established between the marriage act and procreation, the whole question of marriage and sex came under re-examination, first by the founders of the birth control movement who were most frequently a-religious when they were not anti-religious, and later by religious leaders themselves. If married people who love each other sexually, need not thoughtfully consider the natural consequences of their loving, and indeed may positively exclude children from their loving by any means at hand and without regard for established moral law, then certain new patterns of behavior in and out of marriage were inevitable. First, family size would become smaller; and it has. Secondly, smaller family size would involve radical differences in the relation of parent and child, and of siblings; and it has. Thirdly, if regulation of fertility did not mean regulation of sex, then there was the chance that sex might break through the bonds not only of Puritanism but of all self-control, and thus become an end in itself; and it has. Fourthly, if one class of contraceptives did not work effectively, other forms of birth prevention such as sterilization and abortion would receive increasing approval; and they are. Fifthly, if moral law is not the final determinant of whether a particular method of birth control is to be used or not used, then scruples with the use of contraception by the unmarried would tend to vanish, since moral law and it alone really prohibits fornication; and so we take note of increasing sexual promiscuity among the young and new movements to provide even sixteen-year-olds with contraceptive service.

The real problem for the Christian came not as a result of these sociological phenomena, but from the Lambeth Conference of the Church of England. In 1920 the assembled Anglican Bishops expressed alarm at the growth of contraceptive "theories and practices hostile to the family." Ten years later another conference of these same leaders stated that "we cannot condemn the use of scientific methods for preventing conception which are thoughtfully and conscientiously adopted." The wall had been breached so that in this year of 1964 the whole Christian tradition concerning sexual and marital morals is under growing attacks and the Church herself must now reinterpret her basic principles in the light of these new circumstances. No longer—and we say this with sadness —is it sufficient to say this is the Sixth Commandment and here is what it means. Now we have to expose in detail our whole philosophy of life, the revelation of the prophets, of Christ himself and the basic unchangeable conclusions made from them. We must help people see the beauty and vital importance of the Christian concept of sex. We must clearly demarcate those new ideas (which can, without great effort, be fitted in with the Christian religion) and those practices which are completely alien to moral law and therefore must be rejected. The modern Christian may accept family limitation but not contraception, sexual enjoyment by wife as well as husband but not an identity of sexual roles, the enrichment of the love relation of man and woman born of new scientific knowledge but only by spouses joined in holy matrimony and better preparation of the young for marriage but not encouragement of sexual relations for the unmarried.

For all these reasons Dr. Henri Gibert's *Love in Marriage* will be of substantial interest and invaluable help for countless married couples of our time and perhaps even more for those about to accept the great calling of matrimony as their own but are as yet unspoiled by unfortunate experiences, memories, or habits. Parents who want a good background for the Christian education of children in matters of chastity will also be indebted to the author. This is a profound book and yet one written in beautifully simple style; profound because it goes right to the depths of the meaning of sex and married love; simple because its message can be understood by the average educated man. This is a Christian book because the discoveries of modern science are blended harmoniously with Christ's gospel to such an extent that the reader is persuaded how right the Church is when she teaches her

"Good News" on marriage in season and out with all its purity.

Very early in the book Dr. Gilbert goes to the heart of a major modern fallacy and cuts it out at its root—"To conduct oneself sexually," he says, "in the proper human manner calls for more than a science, more than a technique. It is an art, namely a way of understanding life, of sensing its innermost meaning. This art of loving, like all other arts, presupposes an arduous apprenticeship spent exploring the entire scope of the subject of this study." Sex education usually means information, particularly in the areas of anatomy and biology, and recommendations on how an ecstatic union of sexual organs can be accomplished. While not neglecting physical development at every level of age and sex, Dr. Gibert makes his dominant theme to be: Love involves a union of two persons, creatures of God, who come together for His purposes as well as their own, and who by following their better instincts and better reasons, as well as God's law, will thereby find themselves enriched and rewarded.

Young married people will find in his chapter on conjugal relations all the guidance they will ever need. Rarely, too, have I read a chapter on "Continence and Chastity" so well written and done with such authority. He takes up all the major arguments for sexual indulgence and lays them to perpetual rest. Questions of family limitation and birth control are frankly discussed and the most recent medical information on female ovulation clearly presented. It is my fond hope that Dr. Gibert's book will obtain a wide American audience. *Love in Marriage* deserves no less.

Monsignor George A. Kelly
Family Life Bureau of the
Archdiocese of New York

LOVE IN MARRIAGE

Foreword

In every civilized society sex is a conversational taboo save for the rather frequent jokes about it. All important human themes are in like manner favorite topics of banter—religion, death, love—as if mankind hoped to resolve in laughter the awesome mysteries concealed therein.

To broach the question of sex is extremely difficult. It is a matter as vast and shifting as the sea, and to discuss it is to run the risk of either offending or of misleading. Yet it is hoped that these few pages shall have skirted the hazard and that they will serve the adult as well as the adolescent by helping each to reflect upon his own behavior, and by offering in terms as simple and as accurate as possible the explanations that each of them seeks concerning the most important aspects of this com-

19

plex and ever-present problem.

The basic point always to be kept in view is that *the whole human being* is involved in whatever concept one forms and adopts regarding sex, for the sex instinct with all the emotional powers bound up in it not only constitutes the mainstream of our personality but is also the most powerful actuator of most human undertakings. The line of conduct which a human being follows with regard to sex will not only condition that individual's behavior in matters specifically dealing with sex, but will influence the aggregate of human values and ideals in which he will believe. From such a line of conduct will derive in large part the success or failure of a life and the happiness and inner poise of the person. Sex therefore assumes for each one of us a cardinal importance that no one would seriously question.

It is not surprising then that sex should have been one of the subjects most frequently discussed throughout the ages. From the dawn of its history, since it emerged from animality (that is to say from the moment man became able to examine and analyze his very life processes), humanity has been in a questioning mood with regard to sex. From the poems of Homer to those of Rimbaud, from the paintings on the walls of the caverns of Lascaux to the works of Raphael's and Watteau's brush or Rodin's chisel, from the first inarticulate chantings of primitive men to the symphonies of Beethoven and Berlioz, sex has never ceased to inspire every art form. Through ages and cultures, be they of polished stone, iron, oil or uranium, love in all its forms, from the most sublimated to the most sensuous, has ever been at the very core of every human being's concern.

Now if in all times men have been preoccupied with sex, it seems that our own era is marked in this respect by two very particular characteristics.

On the one hand, for the first time in human history, our era has approached the subject with both a scientific and statistical mind. In recent years numerous research projects have been made in this matter. The best-known and most exhaustive is the Kinsey Report; and one of its principal merits has been that it focused the cold, objective light of figures upon what was already known through experience; namely that sexual harmony between two human beings is difficult to attain, a long and exacting work seldom completed, and a precarious accord subject to ever possible discords.

Our times also have a peculiarity, which makes it more than ever necessary for adolescents as well as adults to be given valid sex information. We all live—though often unawares—in an atmosphere charged with a high concentration of eroticism from which there is no easy escape and to which none but the forewarned and forearmed can, understandably, offer any resistance. Sex pervades the press, the advertising media, the movies, television. This erotogenic environment laps at our imagination and assails our senses. All these solicitations have but one direction; to show us sex as being in the service of the individual, with this individual considered as its supreme and exclusive end. In reality human sex is bound to the service of love, not of selfishness.

Here then for the first time the word "love" makes its appearance. The notion is prevalent that love and sex are mutually impervious and develop separately; going still further, some consider love as a decrease or a default of sex, viewing it as a useless, troublesome and even offensive element of sexuality, initially unprovided for, akin to a foreign body or an impurity which happens along to disturb the normal and automatic operation of a physiological function of the same order and same nature as digestion or blood circulation. Under these terms the "mate" is nothing but a means to the attainment of self-gratification.

Particular attention will be paid in these pages to demonstrating that human sex differs radically from this carnal egotism to which some give the name of love, but which is no more than the parody of love, or rather its negation. Indeed, even when viewed on the purely natural and physiological plane without the slightest reference to religion or metaphysics, human sex is the very opposite of egotism since it is the privileged means for a person to present to another the gift of oneself.

It will also be shown that human sex differs in essence from that of the animal, and that even on biological grounds alone there can be no denial of the spiritual aspect in the union of man and woman. Disprove this, and you would not only alter the image of the sex function but disfigure it and slash it, voiding completely one of its vital components by the curtailment of what makes it different from the coupling of animals.

In its essence love is "an impulse towards giving, the giving of oneself and the welcoming of another's gift of self." It creates a disposition of openness "in which the loved one is received and welcomed, with the desire to give in return everything at every plane: emotional, intellectual, physical, spiritual." [1] This longing to be united as one leads to a yearning for proximity, for the closest possible intimacy and, on the physical plane, culminates in "being two in one flesh." This yearning is satisfied in the conjugal act and only there is it utterly fulfilled.

That is why the study of human sex must not and cannot be restricted, as it was in the past, to furtive descriptions of the reproductory function. Sex cannot be isolated from the organism. The question is not so much the giving of advice or the imparting of information, but rather the opening of minds in preparation for the future. To be valid and rational, the study of sex must encompass all of the psychological, social and spiritual domain of love; it must make it discernible that love is a psychosomatic complex which evolves in the human climate of a psychobiological relationship between two beings. Of prime importance is the dialogue between man and woman, and their love must be the gift of self, without which their union is nothing more than a companionate mating, or a partnership of interest.

Although sex has been the topic of thousands of treatises, it remains one of the most mishandled and misunderstood of subjects. The vast majority of people of all ages and conditions have only false, ludicrous, distorted or garbled notions about it. Man is forever asking himself questions about it, but throughout his life he keeps coming up against a long run of difficulties which arise without abatement under various guises, as if man must pay the price of endless torment for the mysterious power to transmit life and for the awareness that such power is his.

The areas in which the young or the adult person is faced with as many problems as in sex are indeed very few. Most adults have some unresolved sexual difficulty; serious or slight, it will by degrees echo through their whole behavior and impair the harmony of their life and their home. Yet how easy it would have been at the outset to fill an early gap or to straighten an errant deviation. Few adults however have sufficiently precise information in matters of sex with regard to its fourfold aspect, the anatomic-physiological, the psychological, the social and the spiritual, to find within themselves the answer to their own problem, and fewer still are able to talk such things over with their teenage children. As if this talk were taboo, they recoil from it, when it really can be the simplest of all things.

To conduct oneself sexually in the proper human manner calls for more than a science, more than a technique. It is an art, namely a way of understanding life, of sensing its innermost meaning. This art of loving, like all other arts, presupposes a long and arduous apprenticeship spent exploring the entire scope of the subject of this study.

Everything is being taught nowadays, with learning aids available in growing profusion. What is purely and simply ignored is not of course learning to "make love," but learning how to put the sex function to the use best suited to each personality. So paramount is the sex function in the wholesome growth of the human person that its education ought to be central in the formation of young people; and yet at the very time their personality is most openly receptive to formative influences, parents and educators too often fail to supply them with the means, readily suited to each individual, to shape for themselves a strong, valid and well-equipped sex personality. The great majority of the young are given absolutely no worthwhile information of a psycho-sexual nature, for a zone of silence is officially created around sex. The sham of false modesty is the chosen shelter, or the game of chance is inconsiderately allowed to play its part, or friends and playmates hardly more knowledgable and at times already deformed are foolishly given the vicarious power to instruct children in something which later will be one of their dominant concerns, and which in the immediate present raises for them so very many problems and difficulties.

This book has been written to treat such deficiencies. First the sexual development of the individual is traced from birth through puberty and it shows how strong the impulses of sex are at *every* age. Then the true nature of human love is described, and the differences between the psychology of the male and that of the female are stressed. Finally, it is shown that respect, a certain restraint and patience are needed if love is to be preserved.

PART ONE

The Psychological Aspects
of Love

I

Education in Love

Throughout life it is the duty of the individual to know how to behave sexually. This means the dutiful foregoing of instinctive and immediate gratifications through avoidance of any triggering within himself or situations that could compromise his moral or biological balance. How thoroughly the individual submits to the necessity of proper sex conduct is of the greatest consequence, for upon this will largely depend at once his moral life and the health of his mind and body.

This is what "sex education" usually means, but the term is not too apt because, in describing a many-sided reality, it puts the accent solely on the physical. But, there can be in this domain no "education" if information is given only in anatomy and physiology. The only valid process here is a self-training of the young which encompasses the totality of his person. A better term than "sex education" would be "education in love," if we may borrow the title of an essay by Doctor René Biot. Such a phrase shows how much more complex and fluid is the reality which must be known. Sex education proper is of course necessary and must be given, completely and with precision, during the prepubertal period, when the child has to be apprised of the particular role of his genital organs; but it must come along only to complement the formation of a balanced "psychical sex," meaning a well-integrated subconscious set of the mind, concerning the significance of sexuality in man and the respective roles played in love by the two sexes.

This training of the human being in the function of his particular sex, that is to say the training of the man and of the woman, is the very basis of any sex education, a primordial element because it is the most unspecific; hence it is the one most likely to leave in the child the deepest and most indelible marks. Whether it be in the matter of games, of work, or of clothing, parents must keep this elaboration of a "psychical sex" in the forefront of their preoccupation so that it will saturate forever the child they are training.[1]

It must also be adapted to each stage of the child's development, for the sexual structure of a human being is in constant evolution from the moment of birth. Many are shocked by the mere mention of sex in the infant. Yet, since Freud, anyone should know that long before the first flush of puberty, the child has a latent sexuality which is part and parcel of his instinct. At any age the "libido" is a kinetic force in humans; at any age their emotional affectivity is linked to their sexuality, to such an extent that there is not a single display of emotion that does not have some proximate or remote link with sex. Precisely because this infant sexuality does exist, sexual training (if it is to be of any value) must begin very early and be spread in stages of sharper explicitness until puberty, then be continued for quite a long period thereafter.

To the nursling and baby everything is feeling, pleasant or displeasing: this age knows nothing except elemental reactions of enjoyment or of discontent evoked by the vegetative process and elicited by whichever part the child's surroundings play in its vegetative life. For many long months the entourage is limited to the mother. Through her the nursing infant begins his discovery of the world; she is the first person he comes upon; his love for her is carnal; his well-being is by her and from her: why would he not be attracted to her who gives him food, warmth and companionship? So begins the Oedipus complex for the mother, a fixation destined to play so large a part in infant sexuality. This is the digestive phase of infant sex, when contact with the mother's breast and the sense of a well-filled stomach give the child very real sensual delight. So too does thumb- or finger-sucking. And so does the emptying of his bladder or intestines, accompanied as it is by a sensation of well-being to which the child is highly sensitive and which Freud holds to be of erotic nature.

At the age of three or four, sex surges discernibly. The

infant becomes aware of his body, "explores" it, and in this search for information about itself, comes upon some areas that are more sentient than others, and there the child dallies. No need at all to be surprised or frightened by this fondling of the genital parts; it is commonplace and normal. Above all, *there must be no punishing nor scolding* as the child would absolutely not understand the meaning of such reproofs. All that need be done is to draw his attention gently to other activities, and all goes well. If fondling persists it is often the sign that the child, right or wrong, believes he is inadequately loved, and he then withdraws within himself and seeks to compensate. Displays of affection for him must then be redoubled, and this is generally enough to put an end to these troubles.

At about this time the child begins to take cognizance of the differences between sexes. Boys are proud to be unlike their sisters, while girls are humiliated and resentful in their assumption that something is missing in them; this is what psychoanalysts call the castration complex. The small girl will ask questions about this, and the moment is here to explain to her that yes, there *are* two sexes; that girls *are* made different from boys, but that "it was not a wicked hand that cut off that appendage which she envies her little brothers." [2] She will be told that all is well as it is, since children need both a father and a mother, each of whom has a particular role to play in the home.

This finally is the age at which the child wants to know how he was born. This questioning must be met without mystery, without embarrassment and without a smile; it must elicit immediate, straightforward and logical replies, in order to still a curiosity which is after all quite legitimate. No attempt must ever be made to avoid such questions, but one must give at the right moment "the answer to each question before it creates a conflict, not however before it has taken shape in the mind."[3] There must be for the child's benefit a revealing only of that which he wants to know and which is within his understanding and unlikely to create for him false and untimely problems; the truth he is told has to be equated to his age. However, since pregnancy in his own mother or in other women does not escape his keen observation, it would be senseless to try to hide from him the fact that children start developing within the frame of the mother who protects and feeds them. When it is thus told the truth in simple terms, the child is mindful from the start of an association between the idea of love and the idea of creation in an ambiance of unselfish generosity which places upon procreation and love the mark of sacredness. The opposite course, the calling out of arrays of cabbages and storks, would have no other results than to distort beyond redress the child's outlook and to make a later revealing of the truth infinitely more touchy.

This early blossoming of sexuality lasts approximately until the age of six. Then another period begins, one of latency. No more questions are asked, and the child even seems in many instances to have forgotten what had been explained over and over again. The reason? New vistas have opened before him, new centers of interest have seized his attention: school, group activities and games, family visits and outings, and so on. The reason may perhaps also be that the child is more or less consciously content with not knowing everything about this thorny subject. Above all and in the majority of cases, this quiescence is due to the fade out of the Oedipus complex. Sexuality redirects itself toward father-son, or mother-daughter identification, and the process allows the child (and the parents!) to live through a lull before the storms of puberty.

Puberty

According to its etymology, puberty is that period in life at which hair begins to grow in the region of the genital organs. In medical terms puberty describes the moment of the first menses in the girl, and of the first night ejaculations in the boy.[4]

Long ago, somewhat naive and over-simple views had it that puberty was a "real revolution," a "second birth," an "upheaval" triggered by the first surge of the sex instinct. In point of fact the development of sex characteristics merely objectifies in tangible fashion the profound changes which went on in deep hiding within the organism through long preparatory stages. Puberty is not a dateline, but a period of transition between childhood and adulthood; it is not a static fact, but a dynamic pass that spans a long term. It is but a moment in a lengthy evolution which will go on for many long years; it asserts itself throughout adolescence, even after physiological pubescence, and it reaches into the planes of psychology and emotions, and up to the complete maturity of the individual. It comes to an end "when a sexuality that began with life reaches its full flower." [5]

It remains true nonetheless that in every domain puberty is the signpost of a capital stage on the journey of the individual toward his complete development. Past this point changes may still occur, but the cast of tomorrow's adult is already molded definitively in broad outline. The plasticity of childhood sets into a quasi-rigid likeness of the adult being.

The growth of the sex instinct

A somewhat lengthier treatment is going to be devoted to this particularly important phase of the individual's evolution toward sexual maturity. For puberty is much more than a simple hormonal surge resulting in the emergence of the genital function. The quickening of the sex instinct is paced by deep psycho-emotional changes. Puberty is a complex phenomenon involving the whole personality and expressing "that profound dictate of evolution in the individual which orders him to break with infant dependency and venture forth in search of his autonomy." [6] The adolescent forsakes the clean, unworrisome and clear world of childhood, but does not at once enter the adult world because he has to go through a critical, confused and troubled period during which he will be particularly exposed to physical and psychical harm. Within him rages "a conflict between those two worlds: the old one, that of childhood, to which the adolescent is tied by his whole education, his feelings, his love for his parents; the other, the new world of adult age after which he aspires with more or less clear perceptiveness, and in regard to which he has yet to become sufficiently objective." (Amelin) The turmoil of puberty is directly proportionate to the difficulties which the adolescent experiences in his straining toward realization and fulfillment of his being, and in the efforts to integrate in harmony within himself the new values he is in the process of discovering. If any problems have been left unsolved so far in his evolution, this integrating of instinct into one consistent line of conduct becomes at times unachievable.

The whole situation of the adolescent with respect to the world about him constantly changes therefore during this period. His psychological evolution, which extends over several years, will depend just as largely upon social, family, cultural, spiritual influences, and upon the reactions they set up, as upon the psychological frame of the individual himself. Puberty indeed "is not a crisis that terminates in the tranformation of the individual, but a reactive behavior in response to conditions of life and to important social pressures. As a crisis, puberty is psycho-social as much as it is psychological." [7]

The two essential characteristics of the psychological manifestations of puberty are their *multiplicity* and their *changefulness*. "Adolescence is a prolonged stage of ir-resolution normally due to lead the subject to become conscious of his autonomy and commit himself to a so-cially integrated mode of existence." Ill-defined as to its time limits, this period is subject to the oscillations of a personality in quest of itself. Virtualities of every descrip-tion are spread before the individual, each one apt to become actually a way of life; all these potentialities which entice the adolescent create the painful but ines-capable necessity of choosing. This is a factor of instabil-ity, since the adolescent instinctively delays the moment of choice so as not to slam the door on other potentials which he vaguely senses will never be actuated: he hesi-tates in fear of cooping himself up too soon and too tightly within the confines of a set future.

What the adolescent experiences

Many authors have described the character traits of the adolescent. If these are mixed and blended in varying proportions, endlessly diversified pictures can be painted.

Here are three of the most noteworthy among these characteristics.

1. *The need for a personal life.* Before he can become pliantly adjusted to his environment, the adolescent goes first into a reaction of opposition and challenge against all the routines and established patterns of the social body. To become adult he must detach himself from adults, above all from his own family. If he does not possess some aggressiveness he can neither set himself free from childish dependence, nor break out of the circle of family conformity. This is the crisis of juvenile eccentricity, this rising in opposition and rebellion against every accepted practice, and the outbreak is timed in the adolescent with the first spark of awareness that he is a self-directing individual in his own right. His primary concern is to assert, through contrariness, a personality fumbling to find itself. As the child feels his independence grow he has a sense of being a stranger in his own family and he aspires after one thing: to be free and independent. This phase is perfectly natural and rightful, a necessary step towards social adjustment. Many a biological adult has remained psychologically a child because he was not capable of those essential wrenchings.

But adults who surround this adolescent often have trouble understanding what he is going through. This incomprehension is quite prevalent within the family, and the years following the start of puberty are rich in conflicts and collisions in the home. "Many parents take very hard any acceptance of such emancipation; the desire is deep-set to keep their child in tutelage, and any show of independence on his part rouses their hostility. They deny him the right to have ideas and illusions of his own, lash him with mortifying remarks and, on the plea that they do not want to 'lose' him, actually prevent him from becoming an adult. The widespread instinctive distrust so many young people evince toward their parents might be viewed—and sometimes justified—as a kind of intuition of danger." [8]

2. *The need for a friend.* The emotional needs of the adolescent are then no longer met solely within the frame of the family, and the emotional crisis of puberty is marked by the welling up of feelings of love or friendship toward outsiders. Children, considering their parents as remote and "square," no longer dare confide in them, but become secretive and reticent. The more they have been held down and constrained, the more of course they will feel distrustful—all the more so if talking about sex has been tabooed in the home.

At the moment he awakes to the consciousness of the world about him, seeing it no longer as a thing for grown-ups but fancying it as his very own, the adolescent feels an urge to compare ideas with a friend his own age. This sense of needing a friend is absolutely essential to his full development. From it derive those all absorbing teenage attachments and crushes, during which adolescents assume the ideas, habits, mannerisms and even the bearing of an object they have seen and come to admire.

Sex now becomes a complex of physical instinct and tender emotion. Love of self gradually makes way for the seeking of a rather vague contentment in nearness to another, and this is the first adumbration of real love. At this age however, especially in girls, this early love generally centers on a person of the same sex. This is the age of friendship or of frenzied admiration for a school chum or a teacher, the age also of secrets shared, of jealousy tantrums, of sacrifice mutually offered, sometimes there are exchanges of tangible tokens of affection, and when quarrels occur there are tears, sulkings, despair, and at times rebellion.

Since the awakening of the senses is in pace with the quickening of the heart, one could fear for boys and for girls alike, that these doting friendships might change into homosexual intimacies. Yet it seems that adolescents, though prone to friendship, are generally very far from associating it with sexual exchange; for them such exchange is the very opposite of the soulful affection which is their representation of uniquely real love.[9]

Not infrequently adolescents of either sex feel genuine disgust at the very thought of the sexual act because they view love only in its ethereal aspect, unsupported by any carnal prop. Moreover

these feelings are the seeds of the ones which some day will draw the adolescent to marriage. The psychological crisis of sensuality during the pubertal stage forecasts primarily the emotional emancipation which will bring a young person step by step to the point of bestowing love, total and integral love, upon a person freely chosen, who will satisfy all sentimental yearnings and meet new sex demands, and with whom life will be shared and propagated in a newly founded family.[10]

The adolescent is indeed looking for the satisfactions, excitements or thrills of sex, but in a manner as yet only indirect, covert and easily sublimated. And thus the needs of sexual satisfaction and those of emotional fulfillment develop together yet independently and, at times, even in reciprocal opposition until they reach, in the true adult, a point of fusion and of harmonious blending which give all of them their complete flowering.

At any rate the first manifestations of adolescent "love" must at one and the same time be "treated with respect— since they are the necessary steps in emotional development—and also be made secure against anything likely to prod the young person into jumping the gun and becoming a precocious runner on the course of real adulthood.[11] The very greatest care must be taken not to have the child think of the awakening in him of the sex instinct as something unclean, shameful or unworthy of his interest.

3. *The propensity for escapism and daydreaming.* The overexcitements of the adolescent period coincide with, and are promoted by, one more salient feature of that age, namely the frequency of wild flights of excitement concerning art, religion, sociology or politics. Hence come those impassioned discussions on love, death, religious belief, money, and the social order, etc. It is a time when all extremes find an echo in a sensibility which is not yet fixated but always on the alert and constantly lying in wait. It is a time of great dreams occasionally destined to

influence a whole life, a time "of intimacy with idle musings, of being far away from reality. Every adolescent is given to daydreaming, as he senses in himself new energies he would like to expend . . . But barriers rise before him, set up by family and society, and so he either rebels in opposition, or withdraws within himself in order to escape in this dreamlike pursuit of great human quests like power, love, wealth. Imaginative reverie is a normal reaction for him and, it must be added, is just a game which he can stop playing at will. Outlets are found in creative poetry or fiction, in the intimate "Dear diary" journals so commonplace at that age. But if the rash of daydreams persists, if withdrawal and escapist fantasy become so deep-seated that the child has no ability to realize that this condition exists, the problem of a schizophrenic evolution is posed." [12]

*   *   *

So much for the broad outline strokes in the psychological atmosphere of the pubertal period. Now for a brief recall of the main physical and physiological characteristics of that age. No great emphasis need be placed on the changes in body and mind which take place at that time; far from going unnoticed, they tend rather to monopolize attention and thus put in their shadow the underlying psychological substructures upon which they rest.

In the adolescent of either sex, weight and stature are of course on the increase; but while so far the overall profile of both sexes was identical, henceforth the particular forms of each are going to become accentuated. In the boy, muscularity will dominate and bone structure will assert itself in a broadening of the shoulders, while hips and pelvis remain narrow. In the girl, fatty tissue becomes more abundant and is so distributed as to mark the difference in sex, gathering about the pelvis, hips and breasts, and thus giving the body its more rounded form. Meanwhile one of the most distinctive changes of the female pubertal period now begins to take place: the pelvis increases in overall dimensions, widening at its front face, while the sacrum assumes a more concave shape. The end result is a lower pelvis and wider hips than one observes in the male, all ordained obviously in view of eventual motherhood.

The burning up of food intensifies, and food intake must be increased—particularly foods high in nitrogen and mineral content.

The heart rate decelerates, as does respiration which at age eighteen becomes entirely thoracic, having until then been abdominal. Lung capacity, in relation to weight and stature, having declined from age twelve to fourteen, begins to increase at fifteen, a fact which explains the lower resistance to fatigue sometimes observed in adolescents.

Puberty is then marked by the appearance of the secondary characteristics of sexuality. In girls the breasts begin to develop at age eleven or twelve, in successive steps of swelling, spreading and bulging of the mammary glands, with pigmentation of the areola or ring surrounding the nipple. This growth of the breasts, along with the development of the genital organs, captures the attention of the child, but is not always welcome; it is not uncommon that little girls, to ward off the teasing taunts of boys their own age, will bind themselves around the chest in hopes of concealing the growth of their breasts.

A parallel development is that of body hairs. At approximately age eleven for a girl, pubic hairs first appear, then grow more plentiful and finally cover the entire area of the pubis, forming in approximately one year the inverted triangle characteristic of the female. Axillary, or armpit hairs come in at age twelve or thirteen, about six months before the first mentrual flow. In boys, pubic hairs put in a slightly tardier appearance at about fourteen; in them the triangle points toward the navel. Face hair first sprouts on the upper lip, then on cheeks and chin. The overall pilosity, or hairiness of the entire body is also modified. In girls *lanugo,* or the soft downy hair of babyhood disappears, though in some cases it persists on face and limbs; in boys lanugo yields to heavier adult hairs, principally on the chest and on the extension side of the limbs.

At a later date modifications of the larynx result in the voice acquiring its definitive timbre, the tone-color peculiar to each sex.

Finally and more importantly the genital organs reach their adult size and configuration at this time of puberty.

The uterus grows larger and, from the globular form that it was, becomes somewhat pear-shaped, curved, with its top bulbous portion tipped slightly forward. The vagina develops, and its mucous membrane undergoes changes. The vulvar orifice which was until now facing forward and visible from the front, becomes slanted and can no longer be seen in standing position. The clitoris develops as do the *labia majora* and the *labia minora* (external folds and inner folds of the vulva) ; the labia majora become permeated with fatty substance and pigmentation, and to a great extent overlap the labia minora.

In boys the genital glands—testes or testicles—begin to increase in volume at about age eleven and continue this development until age seventeen. At about fifteen the penis enlarges and acquires its definitive size. Secondary sex glands develop in this same period.

This whole set of alterations is conditioned, timed and brought about by the entrance on the scene of the sex hormones which until now have been dormant. Stirred and induced by a secretion of the pituitary gland known as *gonado trophin* or *gonado-stimuline,* these hormones account for the most characteristic, if not the most important, phenomena of puberty. They are responsible for those events that mark off time and place along the shifting frontier between childhood and adolescence. In the girl the ovary is henceforth to be subjected to the alternating secretion of the two female hormones, *folliculine* and *lutein* (or progesterone), which are accountable for the two phases of the two menstrual cycles. These will continue to take place until the menopause (see Chapter V). In the boy similar secretions of the pituitary gland start their task of stimulation in the testicles, as much upon the sperm-producing cells as upon those which generate the male hormone, testosterone, and puberty is then distinguished by the first erections and night emissions.

*　　*　　*

Emphatically, parents must not allow themselves to be outrun by these manifestations which cannot be glossed over, nor ignored in silence. They must speak to the child at some time toward the end of the pre-pubertal period, choosing the moment when attention is caught by the growth of the first pubic or axillary hair, and curiosity is piqued by the mysterious transformations that are taking place. However, since the sexual instinct is one of the most violent and least controlled of all, extreme prudence, great care and infinite tact must attend every step. In choosing the moment, the most serious consideration will have to be taken not only of the child's age, but above all of his sensitiveness, his degree of physical and psychic development and his disposition or character. It is quite obvious moreover that things must not be said in the same way to girls and to boys.

It is useless and even dangerous to go into all details in the very first talk, but as puberty progressively asserts itself and the child gradually nears adult maturity, every detail must be tackled in its turn and wrestled with until the child has a complete knowledge. It is therefore a graded program, and the child's age is the grading factor.

Dealing with a girl, one should begin with forewarnings of the impending flow of blood due to be repeated at regular intervals. She should be told briefly of its mechanism and its purpose, namely to place the young woman's organism in readiness to carry and nourish a small child when the time comes. It is quite imperative that the young girl be well informed about menstrual periods *before* their first occurrence. Their unheralded appearance might well risk causing deep malaise, even severe emotional shock leading to neuroses, anguish or reactions of disgust. An untutored little girl, thinking she is the victim of unusual circumstances, of shameful and dark goings-on, wants to run away from everyone and hide.

All the more so if, when she ventures to talk it over with her mother, she gathers nothing more than some new "don'ts": don't go swimming, don't play, etc., instead of information and explanations that would satisfy and comfort. And so, for her, the first manifestations of womanhood can be surrounded in mystery, guilt, shame or at best in unpleasantness.

It is of course totally useless to deal at length with the possible pains and discomfort of the menses, but the girl has to be told that they sometimes take some months to become regular.

The discussion of the father's part in sex, and of the

act of sexual intercourse itself should be held in abeyance until a later time, perhaps at age fourteen or fifteen. There is some value in pointing up how universal is the reproductive function at the various levels of life, but care must be taken not to confine the discussion within theoretical considerations or comparative references to pistil and stamen—the birds and bees approach!—which would not at all satisfy the child's inquisitive mind. One must not hesitate to touch upon the pleasure and joy of physical love, provided scrupulous tact guides one's words. This is at once a simpler and also a more delicate task with a girl than with a boy. It is simpler because the girl is generally much less plagued by nascent sexuality, and much less exposed to erotic fancies and consequent masturbation than the boy. More delicate however, because the physiological details of the sex act will amaze her to a far greater degree, with the attendant risk of engendering in her a long-lasting feeling of repugnance.

The only way to make the whole matter easier is to place the right accent on what it is that sets human sex so far apart from animal sexuality. This is done by showing that sex pleasure, complete and genuine, is unthinkable in human terms and out of reach unless it is viewed as the consecration of a union of hearts which foreruns, attends and enhances the union of bodies. Therefore, this presupposes as fundamental the notion of predilection and choice.

Because the maternal instinct in a girl far outstrips all

other manifestations of sex, it will be of some value to stress the joys of motherhood by underscoring one of the ends of marriage which is to have children and rear them, and by insisting on the fact that children need for their full growth and development a triangular world where father and mother play different but complementary roles.

These are the only approaches to use in telling children the whole truth about sexual intercourse if it is to be given higher values and if the cutting edge of its physiological and animal aspects is to be blunted and deprived of its ability to permanently hurt the sensitiveness of a child.

Later still the young lady will have to be taught to develop her womanly personality, well rid of the fear of the sexual act envisioned and suffered as an aggression, and freed also from the fear of defloration whose painfulness sometimes overrides sexual delight.

In dealing with a boy there is less objection to precipitating matters through a single session in which will be explained the purpose and workings of the first erections, the existence and design of a girl's menses and, with clearness and brevity, the father's share in the sexual act. But with a boy heed must also be taken not to shock his sense of decency.

Though it will be necessary to talk to him of the sensuous delights found in physical love-making, even more care must be taken than with a girl not to overdo the coloring lest the desire be aroused for untimely samplings of a pleasure reserved for adults, but which the youngster is eager to know. It must not be forgotten that the first sex impulses in man are of sensualistic nature, and that masturbation runs high during puberty. Man's sex instinct is directly voluptuous, extremely violent, very demanding and frantically craving for total possession of woman. One must be very careful not to kindle it recklessly.

In the course of the first talk, a woman's role in the family and in society should be dwelt upon, and the boy must be impressed, in regard to womanhood, with a sense of respect, the clearest sign of civilization. This can be done quite easily if the young man has lived a family life that adheres to respect and tactfulness towards mother, sisters, and their woman friends.

*   *   *

For such a delicate task to be well done requires a singularly competent craftsman. Who then must assume the task of giving the child proper love education?

The instructor to be most categorically ruled out, despite centuries-old acceptance, is that blind and unreliable tutor called chance. Constant alertness must be maintained to the fact that the sex emotions of childhood or puberty, expressed or repressed, are of such intensity, and stamp such a deep mark upon the child's soul, that they will influence his entire life. Parents and educators must take heed of those emotional upheavals, and be eternally vigilant to make children secure against the brutal surprises of the wakening sex urge. The best way to do this is to give

them an enlightened, affectionate family education. If
from the very first parents have always known how to answer a child's questions in precise and measured terms,
the problem is at once laid to rest. But if they dodge the
issue, or try to fool the child with double-talk, his aroused
and unsated curiosity will not let up until he has found
for himself the key to the enticing mystery—the key his
parents could or would not give him. So he will conduct
his own research with great thumbing of dictionaries,
medical tomes and paperback treatises; he will compare
his own scanty, haphazard information with that of his
friends, until he manages to put together somehow, in
scraps and disjointed snatches, the elements of this amazing thing.

He is indeed fortunate if the more "enlightened"
among his pals do not take advantage of the spell they can
undoubtedly cast over this neophyte in exploiting his immature notions of sex to their unspeakable pleasure! "A
demoralizing climate is thus created little by little, against
which children are defenseless; they fall into every trap
which their parents wishfully hoped to help them avoid
by adopting the head-in-the-sand attitude and following
the say-nothing policy in matters of sex. Worse yet: everything touching upon sex is henceforth surrounded by an
aura of guilt and unavoidable clandestinity; very frequently also this premature and skulking excitation can
lead to sex perversion."

Now, if one grants that sex education is not to be left to

chance, is this tantamount to advocating or hoping it should be given in high schools and prep schools "scientifically" and "in groups"? Not at all! There are too many reservations to be made to such proposals.

Risks are too great and too easily incurred that young girls will be inspired with disgust for marriage by too crude a vocabulary, or by overly realistic descriptions. Tragedies beyond recall are likely to be precipitated inadvertantly and without the will to do so. Moreover there can never be assembled before even the best of teachers a class audience so homogeneous that the dispositions, temperaments, needs and corresponding expectations of each listener will be identical with those of all the others. In an area so delicately shaded and intimate, wherein each individual has particular sensitivities, the moment, form, extent and duration of such instruction may and must vary profoundly according to each case. Standardization, which is characteristic of group education, will blunder head-on into the differences of psychic and sexual development each child has reached at puberty.

Sex education must be individualized, progressive and adapted to each child's disposition and temperament. It must be given on demand as problems arise. It follows that parents are the best educators in this respect, father for son, mother for daughter. They are the ones in the best position to fulfill a duty which, for them, is imperative. They alone know exactly what is suited to their child, and they must learn and know well the part they are to play.

Unfortunately only a few families are endowed with the privilege of being able to impart with the required delicateness and accuracy the information children expect.

Sometimes parents lack the means of expression, or fear that they will not have the needed tact. Many shirk this duty, or get it done indifferently, in haste and without sufficient preparation. Thus they renounce one of their essential prerogatives, and choose to think, out of cowardice or sometimes on principle, that any intervention on their part is futile. More often still, parents have been unable, as far back as the cradle days, to create the climate of trust which would now allow them to face resolutely their child's momentous enquiries. Either that, or the long-standing ban they have placed and kept on such questions now renders impossible any candid and simple approach. Confronted with these questions, parents have instinctively reacted with a "modesty of withdrawal" and have naively cast a veil over the questions without asking themselves if their child would not gather elsewhere and in much less favored form the answers they have refused to supply.

It must of course be said that parents themselves often lack sufficiently accurate information about the general facts, the anatomy and the physiology of sexual reproduction. Few adults know exactly the true nature of human sexuality because few have carried into effect on their own account the fusion of body with "heart," of the physical with the spiritual.

Be that as it may, every married couple readily admits that "something must be done about it." But while they stay irresolute the time has already passed for a friendly and serious conversation with their son or daughter of twelve, thirteen or fourteen. Such an exchange would give these adolescents, absorbed in the physical changes they are undergoing and in the emotional upheavals which are shaking the very foundations of their being, the peace and light they so anxiously await. But vaccination costs dearly for the parents themselves, since it deprives them of one irreplaceable means of winning forever the confidence of their children. Later they will be the first to deplore the vanishing of that trust.

But someone has to give the children information. Unable or unwilling to make their bid, parents must "pass" and call upon someone else in whom their full confidence can rest—family doctor or spiritual adviser. This person must possess all the qualifications the parents lacked: first, adequate knowledge of anatomy and psychology; then a well-assimilated experience of things human and a fine personal poise in every respect including sex; last and indispensably, he must have been able to solve his own problems. When a girl is being advised, it is preferable that the mother be present, whereas the father's attendance with a boy is often more embarrassing than useful.

Only later, when young people are seventeen or eighteen, can sex education be serviceably propounded and completed before group audiences. They will then acquire through more thoroughgoing discussion of questions on sex and in the light of earlier experiences and personal difficulties, a sense of liberation and the stilling of the wild flights of fancy and the excitation of the senses. This is the time to jointly give instruction to young women and young men about the basic psychological difference between both sexes, and about the different reactions and behavior of man and woman with regard to the physical realities of love. This is also the best means of preventing the possible later appearance of frigidity or impotence in some individuals.

Finally, when engagement time comes young men should be told about the particular character, both more delayed and more complex, of the female climax. They must learn that it depends upon them to create—not only during the engagement period but all through married life—the favorable psychological environment women need in order to be receptive to physical love. They should also be advised that they must learn how to temper their own passion, giving it free rein only after long preliminary and preparatory caresses have set the sexual act on its proper way to successful completion.[13] The feasibility of all this will be explained on the basis of the knowledge we have of the part played in human sexuality by the brain and by psychics. In addition to such explanations, these conferences for engaged couples have the advantage of bringing into open discussion every question pertaining to the intimate life of the future married pair and to give them not only the opportunity, but also the needed vocabulary to talk over every question in their own private dialogue in a wholesome context. The greatest possible extension of such conferences is highly recommended.

*　　*　　*

It is nevertheless not enough, as was stressed earlier, to give adolescents just such explanations as they demand, touching upon physical changes and upon alterations of their psychology and character. Year after year they must be shown how to integrate what they learn into their whole personality while they are apprised also of the social aspect of love. One of the most vexing problems for teenage boys has to do with how they must behave towards girls. The first time they come face to face with the feminine mystery they sense that it exists, but they do not know how to deal with it. They react in either of two ways—and sometimes in both at once—either placing woman on a pedestal, or considering her a counterpart of themselves, subject therefore to sensual demands analogous to their own and making her then an object of their lustful desires. Self-mastery must be inculcated in anticipation of the very real fight they will have on their hands from now on to govern the new and violent impulses of instinct which will surge within them.

Undoubtedly sex education must be considered as being in a plane totally different from that of all other disciplines. Its intent is indeed not the incitement of adolescent curiosity, but rather its satiation and above all the charting of its course. Curiosity in sexual matters, one of the forms of the sex instinct, is generally accompanied by the desire to experience whatever is imagined. Hence the necessity of calling upon will power, and of bridling the imagination. Simple *instruction* is not enough: what is needed is a very real *education,* meaning a system of morality. This is why sex education is so complex and difficult.

What adolescents want is to attain normalcy in sex. It is up to us to show them that "genuine sex activity is neither deviation, nor yet mere coupling of the sexes, but creative effort in man, and motherhood in woman." (Maranon) It is up to us to supply them with arguments to defend themselves against their desirous selves and against others. It is up to us to make them see, with Hesnard, that:

> sexual pleasure is really growth and the source of true joy only when it has ceased being partial and aberrant and has risen as high as a love which is capable of altruism and tenderness. Imperative prohibitions, threats—even if they transcend the physical—may help the individual not to fall, but they are not enough to give him well-adjusted balance. Yet it is only by virtue of balance recovered and maintained that an individual can reach full development and resist the solicitations of sex, until the time when he can fully satisfy and refine them in total love.[14]

This objective is attainable, and once attained can be held, only if two conditions have been met. First and fundamentally, that the child shall have lived from birth in a family group free from tensions, full of real joy and affection; the best love education is the example of a father and mother united in true love. Secondly, that the child shall have been made to see how far apart, in the matter of sexuality as in all others, man has been set from the animal, notably because of the part played by man's brain.

* * *

In man as in the animal the functioning of the sexual glands depends upon two great systems: the hormonal system, dominated by the pituitary body, and the nervous system, whose constituent parts are the brain and the spinal cord.[15]

Man, like the animal, is equipped with a nervous system having reflexes, or reactions outside the control of the will; he is also endowed with strong instincts. But just as human life is altogether different from the animal matter from which it proceeds, so too the very complexity of man's nervous system allows him to go far beyond the purely automatic and instinctive biological limitations of the animal.

Biologically the essential characteristic of the human species is in fact the considerable development of the brain whose structural complexity sets the conditions for the existence of psychic life.

As a result, sexuality in man—in spite of all the animality its external manifestations seem to give it—is a function which involves the whole personality, and this in

58

direct ratio to the development of the brain. Human sexuality is thus heightened in worth and acquires eminent dignity. Desire is not bred by the genital organs but created in the brain and the central nervous system. This is why Dr. Chauchard was justified in stating that "man's principal sex organ is his brain."

Sexual pleasure and the brain

In the domain of sexuality the brain plays a threefold part.

1. *The brain ensures control of sex behavior.* The nerve centers which impel sexual activity are located in the spinal cord. In the animal these centers are self-driven to their function, and the animal is led submissively by the power of its instinct to where the animal must go. There is no escape, no control. This overriding power of instinct casts upon the beast a number of servitudes which have been analyzed by G. Thibon in a masterly way.

The animal is vowed to isolation by the sex instinct for . . .

> beasts seek each other and couple, and there is between the two an absolutely total psychical impermeability. Each, male or female, moves along within its own impenetrable sphere. Their coupling makes one think of pre-determined harmony, but not of sympathy in the psychological sense of the word. If such aloneness could at all come to be perceived consciously it would be the most tragic and unbearable thing.

The sex instinct is war too. No love borders so closely on hate as does purely sexual love. Brutality in the male, ruse and coquettishness in the female are signs enough of tension between sexes. Psychologists who have held that love between a man and a woman was founded in deadly hate between the sexes have not lacked solid arguments. What is the false-hearted *femme fatale* of history—a Delilah, a Cleopatra—if not a mixture of sex instinct and sin, a female into whose flesh has been grafted not a soul that might raise it above its carnality but a "me" which is its corruption. True woman is above all a soul.[16]

Sex instinct also means disregard for personality. What it seeks in the mate is not the individual person who gives it fulfillment, but just its own self-gratification.

In man the spinal nervous centers are overcast by the higher nervous centers of the brain and therefore they come under control of the will. Man then has the power to curb or, if he so wills, to set in motion in himself the manifestations of instinct. This means that in man instinct is not automatic. Like the animal he is motivated by the powers of instinct, but at some point which it is difficult to determine exactly he is *bound* to assume mastery of these powers, to guide them consciously to their end. While the animal is for all time in the inescapable clench of its own instinct, man is actually compelled, because of the very structure of his brain and owing to his own awareness of himself, to exercise dominion over this instinct.

2. *The brain allows the possibility of acquired behavior.* The human brain is infinitely more complex than any

electronic "brain" or the brain of any animal. It makes it possible for us to possess an *acquired* behavioral pattern. Here lies the distinction between pure biological, generative instinct and sexuality.

The pure generative instinct has a narrow physiological and physical definition; it is the instinct tending toward carnal and anonymous coupling. In its pure state it exists only in the animal and expresses itself irresistibly and intermittently at rutting time.

Sexuality, which belongs properly to man, is something infinitely more vast, more complex, more constant; it broadly over-runs the limits of pure reproduction and encompasses every difference between the masculine and the feminine. Every aspect of human personality is susceptible to receiving some coloring or direction from sexuality, in a manner specific to each individual.

Instinct in the animal is directly adjusted to its own ends, and absolutely rules out the question of a selected mate, since any individual of the opposite sex within the species automatically offers the required satisfaction. In man, quite to the contrary, there is a constant invitation and opportunity to select and choose. It is for a certain type of partner to stir his desire, at times with frenzy, to the exclusion of every other individual. This kind of partner to whom we are sensitized and who will determine our behavior is disposed to do so not because of mere chance, but because there have already been assigned within us to him or to her, often without our knowledge, certain identifying marks resulting from various sensory impressions (tactile, olfactory, audial or visual) to which we have ascribed sexual significance, even though of themselves they are neutral in this respect and have no sexual meaning at all. In contrary manner, such complex sensory reactions may turn out to be negative, give rise to certain revulsions, and perhaps bring about sexual problems of greater or lesser difficulty.

Thanks to these sensory messages of very diverse origins and to their conscious recording in the brain, sexuality extends its realm far and wide and approaches the level of psychic and intellectual life. Sex can thereby be integrated in the general pattern of our life. In other words anything, even though not of specifically sexual nature, can be impregnated with sexualness and come under its sway—imagination, thought, will, love, art, ideals, etc.

3. *Man's brain allows him to be conscious of the phenomenon of sex.* The animal, because it is the servant of the reproductory instinct of the species, is submerged in the derived pleasure, but there is total lack of reflective consciousness which could raise it above its instinct. But, because man is endowed with an infinite potential of organic as well as psychic sensibility, he alone among living creatures has the privilege of taking delight in his pleasure. Thanks to his brain he has the power to watch and feel the process of life within him. By the same token however he runs the terrible risk of cultivating sensual pleasure as an end in itself when it should be for him no more than a means to an end.

It is the brain that enables man to experience in love, beyond purely sexual satisfactions, the joys of friendship. The complexity of the human brain allows him to settle his choice upon a loved and desired partner, "forsaking all others"—a capability completely non-existent in the animal. Human love, when it is genuine love and not a deception of instinct, is also friendship. What G. Thibon has to say on the subject is worth considering:

> There is no worse solitude than to be living in the company of someone with whom the sole communing is through sex attraction immediately dependent upon instinct. Flesh as such is not the doorway to the soul . . . But friendship gets through to the object of love, lives its life, espouses its soul. In this way it puts an end to that aloneness within, which is peculiar to those beings who are brought together by mere instinct. Friendship, the result of abstraction and personal predilection, restores in love proper place to the *person* and, instead of making for a necessarily fleeting association of the two self-centered beings, it brings about the stabilized union of two people who have chosen one another and are mutually irreplaceable.[17]

The choice of a partner is desexualized since it is now normally conditioned by the pre-establishing of human social relationship.

Going no further therefore than the realm of physiology we have arrived at the notion of sex psychology and have seen that the latter brings us naturally and at once to the acceptance of the *personality* of the partner.

> In human sex everything becomes cerebral and psychical; inborn, instinctive behavior patterns give way to acquired patterns of conduct. In the field of emotional affectibility, the

blind reflex emotion of animal coupling rises to the level of
conscious delight and a desire to share the pleasure; the ill-
defined need for this or another chosen partner escalates into
the human sentiment of love. The predominance of this
higher psychic element in man sets sexuality free from the
sway of hormonal activity and requires that it be considered
under its new aspect of psychological sexuality. For all its
belonging to a higher order it is not at all disincarnated, but
it does allow human beings to carry out their sexual functions in conditions where the animal in repose and unstirred
by sexual need would be utterly unable to do so.[18]

These pages so far have described the stages of the
human being's psycho-sexual evolution from birth on;
then they underscored the manner in which the development of the brain and the nervous system enables human
sexuality to be profoundly different from animal sexuality. Now the problem of the human couple must be
taken up.

What is readily apparent in human sexuality is that it
flowers to full bloom and receives its complete realization
only in love. Its perspectives are infinitely more numerous and vast than those of the merely sexual plane, which
is only relative, that is to say only a function of a comprehensive whole. Consideration therefore of merely the
genital functions, or even *sex education* in the narrow
sense of the word, is not the fundamental concern. What
must be regarded as essential is an education in, or of
love, a *love education,* taking the term in its true and
total sense: not just a sexual appetite, but above all a perception of what a *human person* is, and of what a social

relationship means. Human love reaches its full meaning when it leads, through the daily practice of *mutual* self-denial, to the achievement of an ever closer unity between two persons, a unity sought after for its own sake.

A long and difficult task, this love education broadens every perspective. Just naming it is enough to suggest how delicate, changeable and complex is the field it must cover. Like all other things which ennoble man and raise him above himself love is slowly won and difficult to hold. Keeping it secure calls for daily acts of will and for constantly strengthened mastery over senses and emotions.

The search for a mate

Human nature taken as a whole is to be found neither in a man alone, nor in a woman alone, but in both together. The nostalgic dream of a human nature totally embodied within one single being was expressed with highly evocative poetic power by certain Greek myths. In his *Banquet* Plato tells how at the beginning of time the earth was peopled with androgynes, man-woman creatures spherical in shape, having four arms, four legs, two heads and two sexes. These creatures attained so high a degree of happiness and power that the gods took umbrage, and Zeus loosed a thunderbolt which cleaved in half these too-perfect bodies. So was born our humanity, thereafter to be wretched and unsatisfied, hungering for a lost and vaguely remembered felicity. Each of us, born as one half of a being once divided, spends his years in a yearning search for the lost half, and this is the mystery of love.

Another legend is that of Hermaphroditus. There was once a young man of surpassing beauty, the son of Hermes and Aphrodite. He could never go bathing without stirring the passionate love of the nymphs. One of them, a water-nymph named Salmacis, could not resist her passion: as he dove past her she enfolded him in her arms, refusing to release her hold until the gods had made of their intertwined forms one single body.

These myths, like all Greek legends, have deep meaning hidden within their symbolism. They express the idea that man and woman are complementary values, that is to say different in all respects but fundamentally one and needing each other. Because every human being is compelled to consider himself as endowed with sexuality, the sense of incompleteness is there, as is also the awareness of the inability to realize alone the fullness of life's experience. To have sex and to acknowledge that one has sex is to accept oneself as incomplete.

This sense of unfulfillment is what sends the human being in quest of a complemental partner to be found through dialogue with the opposite sex. The whole mystery of love lies in the possibility which a couple has to re-create unity out of two distinct individualities. That is

66

why a person can say to the object of his love "I am not one without you."

The sense of being emotionally incomplete appears in the adolescent at puberty, and constitutes the drive toward the opposite sex in the attempt to discover there what he cannot find in himself. The parallel evolution of emotions and sexuality, the passing from a monologue with himself to a dialogue with the other sex is the true sign that sexuality is developing in the properly human way, for it is only when sex can detach itself from its carnal expression without denying it that sexuality becomes a truly human potential of love.

Along the entire scale of animal life we witness the progressive rise of sexuality from the biological level to the psychological, that is to say from pure and simple coupling, without awareness of the mate, to the conscious and deliberate choosing of a particular partner. "This evolution takes with man a substantial leap measured by the development of sensibility, the appearance of genuine love, the full awakening to the awareness of sexual delight, all of which confirms the purposive pre-eminence of psychological union over the biological function of reproduction." [19]

Human love is not unnatural sexual appetite, nor an instinct for pleasure, nor the reproductive instinct; but it is "the aggregate of all possible appetencies of one being for another, as much in the domain of emotions as in the area of sensuality. This mutual exchange, this essential search for a complementary value broaden sex considerably and place it on a higher level. Love is above all the need for a give-and-take relationship between two persons." [20]

This *relationship between two persons* is the very essence of human sexuality because sexuality is fundamentally a social phenomenon. A human being can realize himself to the fullest, can attain and keep good balance of mind and body *only* if treated like a person and not like a thing. In contrary view, however, Sartre and those of his school, consider love a struggle in which one insists on treating the other like a thing, and the other will accept being so treated. But the interpersonal relation of love is not an indifferent, superficial rapport; it is the most intimate of all linkings, in fact a total and absolute fusion of two human beings. Fusion indeed there is, yet it is not identification of one with the other, nor absorption of one by the other, since it presupposes respect for the mutual independence of each one. Moreover it will be achieved only in so far as each of the partners helps the other to develop and assert his personality.

Marriage is really the only human institution which involves complete and total community of life. "By virtue of its own inner logic, marriage demands the pooling of every resource, including the assets of sex as well as those of the mind, the emotions and the spirit. No other association is so extensive, so mandative of the duty to put the whole being into common service. Some other associations entail community of dwelling, feeding, sleeping; they may call for a pooling of financial interests; they may be designed to foster friendship, good-will, sympathy; they may assure mutual help and stimulate teamwork in pursuit of a common goal. But none outside of marriage gives legitimate right to total community of life, particularly of sexual life." [21]

The sexual pleasure shared during a chance encounter with a female partner, even if she gives her consent, is not human sex. For love to be possible, for complete fusion of one with the other to take place, each must "know" the other, as the Bible puts it. And this "knowing" must be carried out not in a superficial fashion, but in that inexpressible manner which is the way and the mark of real love, above and beyond sex, a higher form of knowing the totality of the person.[22] To know, for humans, is to surrender the most intimate of one's self, to confide in another all of one's concerns, joys and pains, to share with someone else one's deepest life. A poet has put it in a play on words made possible only by the Latin etymology of the French word for "know", *connaître*. When broken into its prefix and head-word, *con-naître*, it may be taken to mean "to be born with," born with another to one love, to one unity; at once to form a more unified couple, and yet also to be one's self more than ever.

God has ordained everything so this might be so. In friendship one has only sight and speech to convey affection, but in married love man and woman dispose of their whole body to express to one another their love. They must use it for that purpose, and not to give each other a pleasure that would be no more than physical. In other words, the mutual gift of self will be a language, a conversation; bodies will be the means of expression, ways to a better discovery of one another, to a more complete sharing of life. Grandeur and beauty come to the moment of sexual union from the total of what a man and a woman have been able to express in all the rest of their life together. Sexual union will then be the culmination of past love, and the sustenance of love to come.

To reduce sex to reproduction is to narrow its scope. Reproduction is of course part of sexuality, but the latter extends far beyond the former. The one can no more be restricted to the other than love can be reduced to a matter of epidermis and mucous membranes. Granted that reproduction is indeed the accepted and desired result of the sex union, still love means much more. If it did not, then every emotional reaction not related to reproduction would be excluded from love.

Giving primacy to sex in the dialogue of married life is not an attempt to disregard the text of Genesis, "Increase and multiply." What it does is to separate human sex from its animal counterpart and set reproduction apart from mere instinct. One might even say with Jean Guitton that animal sexuality is given warrant through human sex: "Nature," he writes, "wants love to come about at some point." Love does come about at the level of human sex.

and the animal origin of sexuality gains understanding only through this upward emergence which allows it to blossom into love, outstripping instinct and bordering on the divine.

Two in one flesh

Conscious awareness that human sexuality is on a level that disengages it from animal sexuality does not repress or inhibit the fleshly reality of human love. A harmonious sex life is essential for the proper and full development of the human frame because there is not a single function of the organism which is not influenced and conditioned by sexuality. Man's intellectual activity and even his spiritual life bear its impress. Conversely, sexual harmony requires that the organism itself function well, because the whole physical frame has its bearing upon the sexual functions.

Being united in one flesh means being two in one life. Total community of life precludes the setting up in any way, by one partner or the other, of a life apart, of a life on the side. This community of life is *human:* while it is primarily of the spirit and must not play the part of the beast, neither must it try impossibly to be angelic. It is the realm of purity, the domain of ideals, yes! . . . but it is also a murky recess where deep within us lie the dormant, obscure instincts whose arousal we may expect at any time. Nowhere but in this realm of love do we perceive so distinctly that man is neither angel nor beast; nowhere else do we find a clearer revelation that man's toilsome greatness resides precisely within the narrow and precarious margin that separates in him the beast from the angel. Treading this slim line will permit man to carry out his own proper sexual behavior and avoid both angel-like disincarnation and animalistic behavior. Sexual intercourse must not be underestimated nor overevaluated. It has its own worth, which will be the greater and more enriching as it is more thoroughly leavened with true love.

It is not human to "act the beast," to deify sexuality and set it up as an absolute. Raw sexual appetite is no more a sign of love than violence and brutality are signs of strength. Eroticism grants primacy to the cultivation of carnal or animal appetites and to the seeking of selfish excitations of sensuality; love, quite to the contrary and above all, is communication with another person.

It is not human either to try to play the angel, acquiescing in sexual intercourse as though it were a vulgar, animalistic, degrading and defiling necessity. Angelicized, platonic love is not real love; certainly we are spirit-like in the better part of ourselves, but we are also flesh, and love on a par with all human sentiments needs embodiment and outward manifestation. An expressed feeling flickers lower and dies, like a fire which is not fed its fuel.

We must therefore know how to give sexuality the high

and exact place that belongs to it when it serves to express the gesture of an open-handed giver and not the grasping move of a selfish hoarder. Human love, through human sex, must use the body in the service of the partner's spiritual welfare. It cannot be repeated too often that man's first fault was *not* a sin of the flesh. But it is also true that sin, the divorcement of man from God, did have its reverberations upon sexuality, causing it to deviate toward lust which fixes things of a sexual nature as ends in themselves. Sexuality can turn man away from his spiritual vocation; it can tend to make man the slave of his instinctive impulses, and it can also downgrade the ideal of community between man and woman to the level of a selfish utilization of one by the other. In these terms, man loves woman not for herself but solely for her body as a means of satisfying himself with gross and serious disregard for her dignity as a person.

That is why the question of chastity is so paramount before marriage as well as in its course. At stake is man's moral and spiritual life.

It is chastity that keeps a man and a woman true to their human calling which is to distill the spiritual from the carnal, to cultivate love from the seed of instinct.

II

Sexual Harmony

The first chapter of this book has followed the human being through the various successive stages of sexual and emotional development from birth to the post-pubertal period. It has been established that a progressive and continuing education of the sense of love must be made, and that the validity of such an education rests on two imperatives. The first is that parents should be able to resolve their child's difficulties in a manner timed and adapted to his physical and psychological development and his consequent capacity to understand the explanations that he is given. The second is that this education should be set in the context of a home life characterized by respect for womanhood, by genuine and total love, and by the disposition on the part of the parents themselves to live up to the principles of conduct they want to inculcate in their child.

Now this child, this adolescent has become an adult. Unless he answers a particular call or responds to a special vocation, he is destined to "found a family," and to live out his adult years not in isolation but in relation to another human person. The object of the following pages will be to show how life as a couple must be lived on the sexual level. It is of course assumed that the idea of love as a social entity have been well understood. The matter of sexual harmony or compatibility is extremely delicate and of fundamental importance since after all its absence is the cause of much misunderstanding and the occasion of many divorces.

> "Sexual harmony is realized when both husband and wife experience, preferably at the same moment, the complete pleasure normally derived from the exercise of the sexual act. . . . Their physical union is fully sensed by both only when the male and female climax are simultaneous" (See Chapter V).

The first act of sexual intercourse

How husband and wife live their first nights together is of an importance that must not be underestimated. A discussion of the question of those first sexual relations in married life is mandatory.[1]

Some difficulties may arise on the part of the young man. The normal reaction in facing any unfamiliar situation is one of slight anxiety and worry. It is therefore quite normal for a young man to go through a few moments of commotion when he is about to inaugurate his sexual life as a married man. In most cases, tension vanishes at once and no problem arises. Sometimes, however, agitation so overwhelms the young husband that it paralyzes him, and the wedding night becomes a fiasco. But there is no disgrace at all in not consummating the conjugal act on the very first night: fatigue, emotion, modesty, a fear of hurting the young bride, the untried sense of responsibility as the head of a family and many other factors may explain this initial failure. For a normally sound individual it is only momentary and of no serious concern. Self-control and composure, a quiet waiting for the next night, letting things take their course and not making a mountain out of what is not after all such a difficulty, that is all that should be done about it. Things are helped along if a young woman has been forewarned about such an eventuality; she can help her husband overcome the difficulty by her affectionate forbearance and understanding, and thus on the very first night prove the quality of her love for him.

Difficulties on the part of the young bride are more frequent, at times more lasting, and in fact easier to understand. Two sets of factors give ready explanation as to why she may be reserved or apprehensive when she faces the conjugal act.

For one thing there is her fear of suffering. Voluminous literature on this theme, often reinforced by whispered confidences and more or less veiled references made by her mother, older sister or girl friend have enlarged so much on it that the girl is sure marriage is going to give her a particularly painful moment. Of course the breaking of the hymen does cause slight pain, but a far greater suffering will result when the vaginal muscles become tense and hinder penetration. Since this very tautness is caused by the dread of pain, and of itself causes pain to continue, there is now a vicious circle which must be broken before it creates an incurable condition. Factually, the pain of defloration is comparatively light when deep and true love resides between the husband and the wife, and he can show himself possessed of sufficient tact and delicateness.

In the second instance, difficulty comes from the fact that her girlish reserve has not yet been transformed into womanly modesty. There is a bit of stagefright in her and perhaps a touch of repulsion for the physical gestures of love. Both attitudes are at this time quite out of place. From the very beginning the young woman must give sexual relation its full value as the necessary and complete way of expressing genuine love. Conscious of this, she should readily set aside any apprehensiveness in her approach to its delicate enactment.

In either instance of course the husband must display infinite respect, gentleness, tact, competence and, if need be, even patience if he is to assist his wife in the decisive step and usher her into an acquaintance with a matured sexuality. Many women are for ever indebted to husbands who were tenderly attentive to their needs in the first days and nights of married life, in those moments which are so crucial in setting the psychological course and in conditioning the atmosphere of the new familial couple. Conversely, many women suffer deep and lasting psychic harm from a husband's haste, clumsiness or lack of patience even when they know he is just ignorant or too casual. Their wounds are graver still if he is brutishly self-centered. Either way a new obstacle, often very hard to surmount, is thrown in the path of the normal and desired climax.

At all events some precautions are in order, dictated by common sense yet frequently disregarded. In the first conjugal relations the couple should be free from nervous or physical strain and overexertion. The honeymoon trip should be neither a race against time nor a tourist jaunt. Short itineraries with leisurely stopovers are the best plan. It might be better to have the wedding night meeting await the time of arrival in the chosen place, in order to give the physical and emotional strains of the wedding day time to dissolve and vanish. It is wise also to put the honeymoon trip under the atmosphere of calm, ease and beauty; and this does not necessarily require blue Hawaiian lagoons nor exotic lands. There is no scarcity in any country of regions close at hand, but far from the hustle and noise of the city or the humdrum of familiar places, where the young married couple can give themselves to each other in surroundings that favor intimacy and quiet introspection. Finally, if at all possible, the choice of the very room for the wedding night should not only exclude ugliness and vulgarity, but should assure a setting likely to poetize and romanticize the first conjugal act in the young woman's view. In a word, the atmosphere should be relaxed.

If serious physical or psychological difficulties should appear during the honeymoon, a physician ought to be consulted immediately upon return. The stock phrases, "Everything will be all right," and "Time mends everything" must not be regarded as true. Difficulties of this kind indeed do not right themselves spontaneously, and procrastination quite definitely tends to aggravate the situation.

Sexual discoveries in marriage

Another stage has been passed. The young couple is back from the honeymoon trip and now starting in earnest to "live together." This is the period of the real discovery of love—in amazement at the slow, progressive and delightful harmonizing of two bodies. But it is also the time of the first inklings that marriage is *not* an ultimate end, that the happiness found in loving and being loved is *not* a forever-and-always acquisition, and that from here on things will *not* move along under their own momentum. Let there be a spat or a quarrel, and the whole beautiful treasure seems dissipated, and anguish comes with the realization that the treasure must be gathered again.

Many young couples allow this uneasiness to prevail and impair a sexual accord just barely attained; the harmony fades and dies away, or seems to them to be a distant and henceforth inaccessible dream.

Some authors estimate that only half of all couples achieve sexual harmony in a lasting and enduring fashion. This means that at least half of all women experience only partially, or even not at all, the physical joys of marriage. The accuracy of such a percentage is hard to verify, but certainly the theme of the unsatisfied or partially satisfied woman is among the most recurrent in the literature of all times and lands.

The reasons for such a state of affairs are seldom of pathological nature but predominantly of a psychological order, and this fact points up the baffling complexity of the problem. It would serve no purpose to enumerate the immediate causes of frigidity in women; the better course is to examine the psychological factors which make frigidity appear.

The first one is one of those truisms the French call a *"lapalissade,"* after that famous nobleman, Monsieur de La Pallice, who was falsely reputed to have excelled in giving amazing expression to truths so evident that they had become forgotten or were ignored. Such is the case here: between the psychology of the male and that of the female there is a chasm.

Learning variations in the act of love

Consider the man: he is solidly built, his bone structure

and his muscular system fit him for strenuous effort. He is built for action, naturally combative and dynamic. Optimism is his keynote. He is the founder, head and defender of the household. Initiative and responsibility are his. Upon him rests the exercising of authority in whatever measure he is capable and worthy, not like an authoritarian tyrant but with love. He is called upon to lead and direct, in matters of sexual life as in all others, and to do so he will have to inform his wife about the concepts as well as the facts of physical love. But he is by nature disinclined to demonstrate or externalize his feelings, and therefore he must make the great effort required to express his love in words, gestures and small attentive things to which a woman attaches an importance he deems excessive.

How many men are really able to do this? One may as well ask, "How many are adults?" for an adult is one who has become fully developed in every sense, a full-grown man, as opposed to an adolescent who is a man in the making, in the process of building. Many believe themselves adults, yet have vague, unavowed regrets for those days when, unburdened with responsibility, they were, as children, mere projections of their mothers. The only true adult is the man who is really adjusted to social living, accepts his obligations and assures in himself the rule of reason over instinct and emotions. The precise intent of any education is to lead children out of childhood and into adulthood, into the condition of freedom, of that deep freedom which springs within each one of us from the knowledge we have of our human dignity, and from the conscious and manly acceptance of the constant responsibility thereby imposed upon us of making the rightful choices at all times. Such a freedom is a far cry from the unlimited kind of liberty, uncurbed by any obligations, which has been advocated by André Gide, and claimed as his own by every Don Juan in the world. Despite appearances, these men have never left the infantile stage of egocentrism, and their life will never be anything but an unfinished monologue.

Now, consider woman: she is given to man, at once his dependent and also his complementary equal. Not his equal in the sense of enjoying the same rights and having identical potentialities, but in the sense of having an individual and independent value which is superadded to that of the man for the purpose of perfecting him.

Her physical frame is more fragile and slender, expressing the tenderness, the accessibility and the graciousness required in one who must nurture and sustain. Where man is the active element, woman represents receptivity with its shades of discreetness, silence and effacement but not without real effectiveness, support and incentive. Women need to be guided, and they expect of a man that he will take command, show the way and have the power to draw everything in his wake. They have the right to expect of him strength of character, sharpness of mind and integrity of emotion.

In this sense and within these limits woman is truly
man's subordinate. But she has her own realm, her privileged and special domain where she holds undeniable
primacy. While a man is rough-hewn, sturdy, uncompli-
cated, unmysterious, cast in a simple mold and none too
subtle, a woman quite to the contrary is a thing of sentiment. In anything she does "she evinces a sensitiveness, an
impulsiveness, a bias and even a sophistry that are all in
some obscure way tied in with her whole make-up, which
is always ready to be stirred up and moved without re-
flection." [2] Her entire personality is centered around her
emotivity, and from this trait her every faculty receives
its particular coloration. Her intelligence notably, which
is subjective, intuitive and very deeply tinged with feeling,
is point for point in contrast to and opposition with a man's
intellect, which is positive, deductive, synthetical, concerned with comprehensive views and readily disposed to
make broad generalizations. A woman is sharply percep-
tive of details, and thus reveals herself as being more me-
ticulous than a man, to whom she can yield a very rich
harvest of human experience. But she is prone to see
nothing but details and she runs the risk of being swamped
by them; and then she needs her husband to help her
grade values in proper order, co-ordinate her intuitions
and grasp things in an all-embracing view.

Woman's love turns to objects more immediate, more material than does man's love. Her ideation remains more closely
tied to its embodiments than does his. She was made to sacrifice herself for those about her with whom she is intimately

familiar, she was made to assure humanity's immediate development. Man, on the contrary, is dedicated to a more general giving of himself; his mission is to exert himself—and frequently to waste himself—in pursuit of ends no less real of course but often less proximate in time and space. Woman attends to the substructures of humanity, man to its superstructures. (G. Thibon)

It is not at all desirable that there should be any turnabout in the exercise of these complementary functions. In brief, *woman clings to concrete things and resists abstraction; man follows concepts, giving them precedence over facts and feeling.*

Another difference, to quote G. Thibon further, comes from the fact that

in woman affection is infinitely less dependent upon intellect than it is in man. There exists in her a kind of autonomy of the heart. A man loves a woman for her qualities, having or thinking he has reasons to love, and seeking to justify his love before his own conscience. But a woman will love a man for his own sake; in her, love is reason enough for love, and the reasons for loving merge with love itself. The man will say, "I love you because you are beautiful, because you are good, because you are sweet and gentle, because . . ." But the woman will simply say, "I love you because I love you," For a man, to love is to prefer; for a woman, to love is to spurn comparisons.

G. Thibon goes further:

Woman's love, precisely because it is blind love, because it has little need for reasons in its support, allows a clearer view of the loved one and feeds on fewer illusions. Insofar as her love is independent from her intellect, this faculty in its turn

85

can function independently from her love . . . [and so] very unlike a man whose love, bound as it is to judgments and comparisons, feels threatened by revelations of shortcomings in the loved one and reacts by lulling itself in illusions, a woman can indulge in the luxury of being quite open-eyed and clear-minded about the man she loves, without having her love impaired in any way. Her love, going beyond the trivial and interchangeable qualities which too often motivate a man's love, her love I say reaches the unique and unchanging substance of its object. In its spontaneous surge it outruns disappointment and does not need the supercharge of illusions. This is why one so often meets a woman who is glowing with love and admiration for a man, but who nevertheless is completely aware of all his weaknesses. This is also why a man is able to let a woman see him for what he is, even in the lowest depths of his innermost being, and still not jeopardize her love.[3]

That the temptation to be unfaithful should assume a different form for each sex is also worthy of explanation. For a man the predominant lure in most instances is purely sensual attractiveness. As soon as sensual curiosity is satisfied, nothing else remains to keep the man close to his most recent conquest; without lingering he moves on to the next, or goes back to his wife whom he has perhaps not ceased loving. Woman's temptation to infidelity, on the contrary, is born of a need for affection, tenderness or protection, and is to be satisfied elsewhere when it is not met at home. If she gives physical consent, it is not only because "the flesh is weak," but also because her emotions have become fixed upon a different man. Because the motives for such a liaison run deeper than those which underlie a

man's "pass" or chance affair, her affair is harder to termi-
nate, and therefore much more of a threat to the peace
and continuation of married partnership.

* * *

Any form of life requires the right environment for its
full flowering. Because of her constitution, her physiology,
her aptitudes and her singular disposition, woman is assigned the matchless role of giving human life its climate,
its atmosphere and its inner setting. She is the soul of the
home. For months, her body is the close biological milieu
for the child she carries within her; and she extends this
physical fruitfulness into the moral fertility of the psychobiological compass within whose limits the child will grow
and develop. She is going to shape the first features of his
mental and moral consciousness as she shaped his body.
There is no one who is not aware of what he owes to his
mother, be it the adolescent who is discovering the world
with its beauty, its pleasures and its allurements, or the
adult who has been hurt by life or engulfed by his own
weaknesses. For all men, a woman remains a haven, a
sanctuary and a store of strength and comfort against difficult times.

The task before her is always a labor of love. "A woman
never becomes a woman in spinsterhood: she cannot find
and realize herself in egotism. The key to the soul of
woman is in the gift of self, in her tendency to center on
others." (Gina Lombroso) Her happiness is always linked

87

with the happiness of someone else, of those she loves and whose love she needs.

> A woman seems to find her joy and full realization in love, in the giving of herself, in dedication and self-sacrifice. She feels the need to care for others. This longing to always give more of herself . . . is what sets woman in such sharp contrast to man who is essentially egocentric in the deep sense of the word. A woman cannot quite understand a man's way of loving, the way he has of giving himself without any loss to himself, remaining his own integral self, unable to sacrifice for love his own plans, ambitions or personal aims, while she recoils from no sacrifice and is ready to renounce anything that is not the love of which she is possessed.[4]

* * *

Too often a woman thinks that for her to accept being a woman would mean renouncing everything she envies in man. Some women feel that it means settling into a kind of decent and banal mediocrity and feeling satisfied to be a charming but useless creature. How far this is from the truth! Woman must know herself and accept herself as man's complementing value, indispensable to him and to the world at large. There is no such thing as feminine inferiority. Woman is neither "an ivory and moonlight goddess" (André Maurois), nor "something between a man and a eunuch." (Simone de Beauvoir) The emotional and imaginative propensities, which are distinctively characteristic of her, cast her in a role she cannot side-step without risks and harm. She is "gentleness and tenderness in this world, and she must agree to remain just that." [5]

88

Nowadays, however, when she is confronted with social and professional obligations in what is so often called a "man's world," she has great trouble in putting her specific instinctiveness into harmony with current cultural trends.

It is very difficult for either sex to acknowledge and understand the emotional reactions of the other. They do not have the same acuteness, nor the same repercussions; they are not on the same "wave length."

Because they are complementary and therefore different, the two sexes always remain somewhat opaque to one another. More than that, the love which joins them lives in fact upon this reciprocal mystery, being founded to some degree on the impossibility of complete mutual comprehension. Friends are attractive to us because of what we know of them; woman, because of what we do not know, and this is a fact that must be recognized. Many a married man suffers disappointment because his love is burdened under too many intellectual demands: he would like to possess his wife through the mind as much as through the heart, forgetting that a woman he could understand to such a point would be one he could no longer love. She would cease being a woman, that is to say the strange unknown who completes him . . .

In couples, moreover, the exchange of love always brings about some identification. As woman's emotional affectibility meets man's ideational love, its compass becomes more universal; conversely, man's idea-motivated love acquires more tactful concreteness as it comes in contact with woman's objective tenderness. Married life renders to husband and wife the greatest service a limited and one-sided being can expect, namely, to be rescued from itself and from its own limitations.[6]

It is often up to the man to help the woman find and accept herself. To do this he must have a good understanding of her psychological disposition, of the hardships inherent in the menstrual cycle and of the weariness resulting from household chores. In regard to these, he ought to lend an active, effectual and constant hand in their discharge.

Sexual urges of man and woman

There is then considerable difference between the psychological framework of a man and a woman. Therefore, it is not surprising if their sex behavior is found to differ just as substantially.

Man is driven to coitus by a violent instinctive impulse whose very violence goads him to seek satisfaction as quickly and completely as possible; a very short time may elapse between the moment he feels the urge for sexual intercourse, and the moment of climax. Inherent in man's nature as a male there is a physiological self-centeredness quite apart from the controlled attitude of an individual man who would choose to be unconcerned about his wife and think only of himself. There may often be, and in fact there often is disassociation between a husband's love for his wife and the sexual relations he has with her. Barring cases of deviation, any man may have physiologically normal intercourse and reach the climax with a woman

90

he does not love, without ceasing to love his own wife. His physical satisfaction, in whatever degree of pleasurable quality it may vary, knows very little variation in its organic values.

Things are definitely not so in a woman. Climax can be hers only in the measure she makes sexual intercourse an act of love, account of course being taken of differences in temperament, education, moral sense, social background, and other factors. She will never reach climax with a partner she does not love or admire, or one she does not feel is superior to her in some respect or another. Even with the man whom she loves and has chosen she will always experience some difficulty in adapting, for she is not driven to intercourse by instinct, but only directed to the conjugal act by her love for her husband.

> It is not enough that she *know* this love exists: she must live it, *feel* it as an emotion . . . This love must *animate* her flesh, penetrate and stir it, become *embodied* within her . . . Then will be born in her the desire to use every means of expressing the love she has for her man, the urge to give and receive, making physical exchange of words, gestures, looks, caresses of closer and closer intimacy, all in the direction of the conjugal act considered as the most complete means of realizing the closeness, the mutual innerness and finally the union of two in one flesh. Their fusion in the flesh is sought by them as the sign of the union of two personalities at all levels: of emotions, feelings, intellect and spirit. Once it is consummated, the union of the flesh consolidates the unity of the persons.[7]

In a woman therefore *the heart moves the flesh*, but the

flesh in turn reacts upon the heart by quickening love. With the one bracing the other, a wife attains the plenitude which gathers all the powers of her being, makes them as one, and makes her own being as one with that of her husband.

This is why a woman, much more readily than a man, understands "the wonderful and necessary alliance between the emotional and the physical." (Charles Rendu) While man's climax is primarily a medullary (spinal) reflex, woman's sexuality is keyed to predominantly psychic stimulants, as much in the distant preparation to the sexual act—she requires courting—as in the moments just before its enactment. "In a man's sexual arousal, sensation precedes sentiment; in a woman, sentiment precedes sensation . . . and sexual union can be for her only the conclusion of a period of emotional preparation." [8] The physiological readying of the female parts for copulation is brought about only if the emotional climate is favorable.

> Granting that a woman is much less carnal than a man in the actual exercise of sex, she is much more so in the soundest refinement she gives to it. Interpenetration of fleshliness and spirituality is characteristic of her to a degree unknown to the opposite sex; she puts more soul into the most carnal emotions than does man, but on the other hand she clothes the concepts of the intellect in more carnal a garb than he does. It often happens that the more a woman is deprived of complete sexual satisfaction, the more affectionate she becomes; her sexual passion, less localized, less violent and less animal, to speak clearly, than man's often finds nearly adequate satisfaction in very innocent displays of tenderness. Unfortunately, the same caresses which vicariously replace for a

woman complete carnal possession, serve only for man to open the way to full sexual seizure, and far from appeasing instinct, whip it to greater frenzy.[9]

Love is a permanent construct on the emotional plane, and also on the physical plane, but there it is often a compromise. This is because feminine sexuality, particularly in a young woman, is much more diffuse than its masculine counterpart and shows up in substitutional manifestations like flirtation, sentimentality and a tendency to reverie. It lies much less close to the surface of consciousness than it does in a man, yet is undoubtedly there. "Woman is very much more able than man to break free from sexual impulses. Many a young girl turns to love only for sentimental reasons in which physical desire has no part. Many women are quite satisfied with chastity, while others take to love without its physical pleasure." [10] The young girl may think her sex instinct is non-existent, but it will awaken as she grows into womanhood and gradually assume its proper complexion. While nearly every young man reaches marriage with very precise notions about the nature of sexual pleasure, the girl, quite the opposite, is utterly ignorant of the kind of sensations she is going to feel, and that even when she has been very well informed in theory. A period of adaptation is therefore the absolute norm, and feminine climax can take place only after a more or less extended period of sexual "breaking-in." But though the absence of pleasure for her is quite natural in the beginning of wedlock, its persistence is unusual if the woman is psychically sound.

A woman is indeed slower than man in opening herself to physical loving, first because she needs to put love into her physical sexuality, and secondly because at the start she is under some handicap. There is still another difference in the behavior of both partners, a difference whose cardinal importance is matched only by the degree to which it is disregarded: a woman's rhythm in the curve of sensual enjoyment is appreciably slower than that of a man (see Chapter V). Although it is the source of many a complaint, this retardance is really a valuable characteristic in that it teaches a man to linger over a pleasure he would otherwise devour avidly and in gluttonous haste. It also imparts the greatest worth to all his gestures of love.

Most of the steps leading up to the climax are, of course, independent of control by the will and automatically reach their conclusion after they have been initiated. It is nonetheless true that in the human species the nerve centers commanding such automatic activities *are* under the control of the brain and, consequently, of the will. Humans therefore have the means to play with them, either by putting the brake on genital sensations, or by calling upon conditioned reflexes and psychic reaction. All too often young men give their instinct its head, unable or unwilling to hold the reins; and so their climax is reached at a fast pace while their wife is still at the start. They must learn, from the very first moment of married life, to master and control their reflexes so as to maintain erection and delay penetration until their wife is in readiness. Reacting against the physiological selfishness which has been shown to be his, the husband must make room for love in the conjugal act, and out of love for his wife, delay his own reaction to the slower cadence of hers. He leads, but he must not seize his own pleasure without regard for his wife, as this would amount to treating her as a thing, not as a person. He must also be self-disciplined in the matter of how frequently intercourse shall take place, learning not to separate love of hearts from love of bodies.

As head of the home he must educate his wife sexually, but he must never forget the responsibility he has to assure her physical happiness. He should use every means to help her give herself, being ever mindful of the oft-repeated truth that a woman cannot give her body unless she also gives her heart. This he will manage to do if he wins the trust of his wife and is able to receive with infinite tenderness and thanks, and even sacred respect, the gift of herself which his wife makes to him, a gift which, initially at least, always has upon it, to some degree, the sign of sacrifice.

Some causes of sexual discord

Sexual harmony in marriage is not to be under-estimated. It is absolutely necessary.

If sexual intercourse is perfunctorily raced through in minutes, to suit the instinctive urge of a husband who has no concern for his wife's feelings and emotions, the woman will then be physically and psychologically at a loss. Things are all right for him, and if, as is generally the case, he does not consciously realize that things have not gone well for his wife, he concludes—and sometimes she does too—that she is not normal: she is frigid! He knows this the way he knows that she has blue or green eyes. Such a conclusion is a profoundly regrettable thing; but very little can be done about it unless every young husband learns how to conduct himself sexually in a manner that will induce the wife to evade this alleged frigidity and to desire and enjoy the same delights that her husband does.

But the lack of sexual harmony is not always attributable to the husband's selfishness. Once human beings have freely chosen to give their life a certain orientation, then all the consequences of such a choice must be accepted. And so a woman who has selected marriage must not only give herself to her husband without reservation, but must do her utmost to ensure her own full share of sensual enjoyment. On this matter, many young women entertain certain doubts and second thoughts; in their view, sexual relations are only a supplementary thing which one tolerates, but which might be eliminated without any impairment of the quality of love. They feel that after their curiosity has been satisfied in the first nights of marriage they might well do without those playful frolics, even though they

96

accept them because, after all, a husband has to be pleased, or it is the only way to have childen, or the law of their sex ordains that they must put up with such things. Their attitude is one of indifference, and they try to justify their passiveness by telling themselves that it concerns or bothers no one but themselves, and that their husband finds his satisfaction and gets his fill of it as often as he wants. However, they have nothing but disdain for carnal intimacy which they consider vulgar and degrading, and they let their husband know or feel that such is their attitude, looking down at him as a slave to matter and to his instinct. They lend, but do not *give*, their body, surrendering it without yielding their heart. They treat their husband like a beggar and give him the humiliating sense of being tolerated. But very soon they begin to find him quite unbearable, and all sexual intercourse becomes an irksome task to which they lend themselves with less and less willingness. As they become tensed and strained, their pain and disgust increase in proportion; their exasperation grows deeper because they feel or know themselves at fault. Even if their husband continues to show them consideration and forbearance they cannot help taking a dislike to him. Thus in practice a home is broken. Conventions and propriety may keep it under one roof, but unity is irretrievably lost. As often as not the husband will grow weary of it all and, with some scruples and hesitation, will set out to find elsewhere what he had every right to find at home.

All this points up how completely wrong it is for a woman to rationalize, consciously or not, her acceptance of an alleged frigidity—it were better called pride! The conjugal act, an act of love, is an act of mutual giving; but a wife can take part in the exchange with real activity *only to the extent she herself enjoys complete satisfaction;* therefore *she has absolutely no right to be disinterested in the pleasures of intercourse.*

Quite to the contrary, she must give full range to her energies, her will and above all her love in order that her surrender shall not be just a case of nonchalant *laissez-faire,* but a real and total gift of self, not only consented to, but actually desired. This is the only way for her to avoid remaining unsatisfied and to reach, in union with her husband, the wonderful stage of full development and psychological balance wherein can be maintained the family climate of happiness so suitable to them and to their children.

Far from retracting, the wife must help her husband discover the deep reactions of her feminine psychological make-up. She will teach him not to separate the body from the heart. Even if she finds him a bit clumsy, as young men often are, she will show him how to make of his every intimate caress a manifestation of loving tenderness. With simplicity, and in the trust she shows in him, she will help him triumph over himself and become himself to the fullest. And thus she can give proof of her gratitude that he initiated her to love and introduced her into the world of physical sex delight.

98

For both of them the conjugal act is a great, unique and precious occasion to rise above selfishness, leave solitude behind and renounce pride, all feelings which find some harbor within the human heart. The sexual act of a married couple will be the more unifying as each partner becomes less concerned with self and more concerned about the other, as each seeks more to give one's self, body and soul, to the other, and to receive the gift of the other.

The conjugal act does not consist primarily in seeking to fill one's own void, one's need for tenderness; nor is it a search for surcease from the hard drives of life; still less is it a passing self-gratification. It is the meeting of two persons who know what they mean to one another, who freely give themselves each time to one another in high desire for each other's happiness.

Because it is all that, because it is a great moment of communing in mutual love, married intercourse is also a moment of great joy: a joy felt in the body, not to be gulped with selfish gluttony but open-heartedly accepted with simplicity, as God's children; a joy echoing louder still in two hearts, in the mutual gift of one person to the other, in the very strong feeling of communion of those two hearts through the mediacy of two bodies.

III

Continence and Chastity

"Sex" education as described in these pages has for its aim to teach men and women to become sexually well-balanced individuals, fully conscious of the dignity of the human being. Under threat of being mutilated and garbled, sex education must spell out the moral discipline which will enable adolescents as well as adults to restrain the impulses of sexual instinct, to resist all solicitations and to control their sexuality.

The animal, totally held in the thrall of its reproductive instinct, becomes adult only to transmit life. As soon as it is enabled to do so, the beast becomes subjected to an urge it cannot resist; it is an individual subjugated to its species. This is not so in mankind, where the individual is not the servant of the species. There is a great difference between sexual *need* and sexual *desire*. The notion of need implies a vital necessity, as for example the need to eat.

Sexual desire is indeed an impulse aimed toward the per-
petuating of the species, but it is not at all a necessity involving the life of the individual who is moved by it.
Man's power to transmit life is not an inescapable burden,
and this makes him the only living creature capable of
celibacy. On the other hand, however, a human being can
find full flowering only in the satisfaction of deep impulses, among which sexual desire ranks undeniably high.
The question can therefore legitimately be raised whether
the individual may reach full development equally well
in the absence or in the presence of sexual activity.[1]

Continence and fidelity

There are innumerable wrong notions having wide
currency with regard to sexual questions. One of the most
prevalent and solidly anchored ideas deals with the alleged
impossibility and even the harmfulness of continence on
the one hand, and of faithfulness in marriage on the other.
The matter is so important that it requires thorough
examination. It will be considered from two points of
view: as it applies to the unmarried, and to those who
are married.

* * *

Continence before marriage is often accused of pro-

moting in a young man approaching sexual relations in
marriage for the first time a state of impotence born of
inexperience. It was granted earlier that he may and does
at times have some trouble, but this must be imputed not
so much to his earlier continence as to a condition of anxiety or overriding emotional tension that might just as
well exist in the instance of extra- or pre-marital relations.

With this specious argument laid to rest, what is the
value of the question? In strictly physical terms and aside
from the danger of venereal disease, sexual activity has
no adverse effect upon health, provided it is not too pre-
cociously nor too strenuously indulged. On the other hand,
no case can be made on the basis of conservation of health
for requiring sexual relations for men or women before
marriage or outside it. Psychologically and morally such
relations offer no incontestable advantage; quite the reverse, they present a number of drawbacks, chiefly that
of distorting from the very first a young man's concept of
womanhood.

Indeed if the young man does not practice chastity, he
turns either to masturbation, or to relations with prostitutes or a mistress. In either case, divested as it is of
emotion and stability, intercourse becomes no more than a
degraded exercise of human sexuality. It is no longer an
expression of love, but merely a means of physical enjoyment.

The brothel customer soon learns to hold woman in
deepest contempt. Intercourse with a prostitute, that

nameless female, has only the *appearance* of normal sex relations; it is in fact only a slightly improved form of masturbation, but it remains inadequate as a satisfaction of the sex impulse because the woman is not moved in unison. The mercenary quality of such relations makes a woman just a thing to be used for selfish purposes; but worse than that, prostitution is sexuality without love. Two human beings cannot be united by physical pleasure alone. Chance love making, which makes for no love, may give physical gratification and even keen delight, but only at the price of a dismal degradation of two bodies. A human being needs love, not instinctive sexuality. It is not surprising that bawdy-house intercourse, like masturbation, should leave its practitioner unsatisfied, bitter, disgusted, dejected and lonely; to him the Latin aphorism does indeed apply, *"Animal post coïtum triste*, Sad is the beast after coupling"! Even in wedlock, couples who do not know how to go beyond mere flesh are plagued with somewhat similar emotions. Flesh alone soon generates weariness and discontent. Sexual intercourse reduced to mere sensual pleasure is rendered unnatural for it does not automatically unite two personalities. It is a factor of union and communion only if it allows two hearts to meet and give themselves one to the other.

Consider the young man in companionate relation with a mistress. He may have genuine respect for her and be bound to her by real affection. But their relationship, lacking any official status and subject to disengagement at the whim of fickleness or boredom, implies in its very nature the possibility of cancellation and discard. It is therefore a deception and a lie in the face of a woman loved and allegedly respected. Moreover, fear of childbirth opens the way with practical certainty to the use of contraceptives, and these, quite apart from the danger to the woman's health inherent in their frequent use, tend to further diminish love.

As for the Don Juan playboy, he is the perpetually unsatisfied fellow trying to find himself in his conquests. His habitual need for change and turnover is witness to a lack of equilibrium and stability, and the sign of an undeveloped sexual aptitude constantly in search of completion. What he wants from love-making is not the tenderness or sweetness of a woman, nor even the occasion to give play to normal sexuality. What he is after is pursuit, hunt, competition. The pleasure he takes in conquering and possessing a woman—and the more out of reach she is the more he craves her—deeply overshadows any need for affectionate attachment. Looking for sexual pleasure only in change, he wanders ever farther from the true psychological fulfillment found only in genuine love, with its pleasurable sensations as well as its obligations. This is so true that in order not to limit the free range of his pleasure he carefully guards against any emotional involvement with one woman, lest he deprive himself of others. His interest in any woman dies the very moment she thinks she has tied him down by yielding her body. In the end, instead of happiness, the Don Juan reaps nothing but bitterness; his is not the fullness of joy, but the void of disillusion. Psychoanalysis explains the Don Juan complex partly as a nostalgic search in a thousand women's faces for the lost mother image, and partly as a violent hostility toward the father who is endlessly tracked down in the person of love rivals and cuckold husbands. It might be noted that this interpretation by analysts receives support from "the classic literary myth of Don Juan in which the feeling of guilt, inseparable from this complex, is represented by the statue of the governor, image of the father-judge." [2-3]

Attempts are made to justify or excuse Don Juanism in the name of an instinctive masculine tendency towards polygamy. In answer to this, it will be worthwhile for the reader to consider the following quotation from G. Thibon's oft-cited work:

> There exists no such thing as polygamous instinct. [Sexual] instinct as such—I mean instinct considered in its purely biological sense—free of all spiritual coloring, is neither monogamous, nor polygamous. It is essentially neutral with regard to fidelity or change, because it does not bear upon these classifications. . . . The sex instinct of the male animal is keyed to *the female* as such, and is utterly indifferent to its being one female or another, the same female or a different one. Undoubtedly, if a different female appears, the male will covet her, but desire will be aroused by the *femaleness,* not by the *otherness.* The male will be adequately sated in the same female, the one he possessed yesterday, or the day before, or last year, provided she meet the required physiological conditions . . . [But] what drives man towards

polygamy is *curiosity,* the sin of mind infiltrating instinct. Pure instinct wants the *other because she is a woman;* curiosity wants the *woman because she is another.* To believe that the sexual drives of a civilized man are made solely of instinct is the greatest of delusions. No one knows to what extent, in this matter, instinct may be serving a man's willfullness for sex power, his thirst for sexual knowledge and dominance. If this were not so would we see so many men devote so much energy to seducing women who are quite often inferior, in physiological terms, to their own wife?

When a man is in the midst of the struggle to remain faithful to the woman he loves, the contest is not between ideal and instinct, but between two ideals in conflict, and in spiritual conflict at that. The ideal of monogamy is at war with that kind of negative ideal which results from the sexual instinct becoming impregnated and depraved when touched by the appetite for change, conquest and sexual possession. The monogamous ideal is in combat against one of the many variations of that lying and Hell-begotten thirst for the infinite which has been consuming man since the first sin. Fidelity in marriage is not a physiological problem, but a moral one: if the soul is monogamous, in depth and with simplicity, instinct will follow suit. One can repeat Christ's words, "If your eye is simple, your whole body will be luminous." [4]

The individual's real sexual worth is not measured by just any manifestations of the libido, nor by just any kind of genetic activity. Masturbation? . . . It is attributable to infantile self-gratification. Resorting to a mistress? . . . It reveals flight from obligations. Woman-chasing? . . . It indicates psycho-sexual immaturity. All these activities are just so many displays of an ill-developed or blocked sexual instinct.

In the final analysis, for the unmarried, chastity is the only response having human values. It has no physical or emotional drawbacks, provided it is neither a repression, nor impotence, nor a scorning of the flesh, but is truly the toilsome and fully conscious mastery over instinct. This mastery needs to be found in three kinds of people: first in the adolescent who can become a man only by learning self-control, then in a person whose calling is other than matrimony, and finally among married couples momentarily apart. This domination over sexual instinct is rare and difficult, as difficult as being human. Most people can do no more than try painstakingly to achieve it.

Chastity in marriage

When love is truly human it gives predominant stress in all areas to the idea of exchange, of dialogue. This should be taken to mean that the individual will be sexually fulfilled only and exactly in the measure that the psychic and the physical components of love are in attendance. A human couple assumes a meaning when two persons start out together in search of love and unity. Each couple must consider its own sex life as the privileged expression of mutual love, as well as an element of its oneness. "The sex act, practiced under conditions that are favorable externally and above all internally, leaves after it not sadness, but a happy and optimistic sense of relaxation composed of deep satisfaction and touching expectation in the promise of new delights. It is the assertion of the joy of living." (Hesnard) In all other circumstances the sexual act is so devalued as to hinder, not help fulfillment.

All that has been said has shown clearly enough that the gift of one spouse to the other requires on the part of both persons a large amount of generosity. It also demands great self-control. This is the last point to be developed here.

Among the forms of self-control, continence is of special importance. Every life, and above all the life of a Christian calls for self-denial. In marriage, renunciations are many, and the most difficult to understand and accept is continence. That is why it must be discussed at some length.

Marriage is not indeed, as is commonly believed, one of those easy solutions. Quite the contrary, it calls for the practice of a rugged and austere asceticism; different, of course, from that exercised by the unmarried layman or the priest, but posing for the married couple problems just as hard to solve, especially if couples have not achieved the unity of hearts and bodies which this book has stressed as its central theme.

Chastity is in fact part and parcel of the vocation to married life; it is not incidental, nor adverse, but quite essential and fortunate. There will be periods when love will be enriched by carnal union, but also times when continence will enhance it.

Continence is necessary in the first place because it will be imposed upon a couple by life itself in time of illness, unavoidable separations, periods preceding or following the birth of a child, and so forth. It is necessary again because births must be spaced at reasonable intervals. The couple's creative power, a manifestation of love, is not aimed at selectivity in the production of a race of superior humans, but at bringing into this world and raising—that is to say leading to adulthood—human persons. This can be done only if children are allowed to live in material, psychological and moral circumstances which will provide for them that self-determination which is the special mark of true adulthood. Each couple must therefore be concerned

> . . . about measuring the number of its offspring against the actual and concrete capability it has to educate them. Birth control is demanded by the very concept of the married couple in the human as well as the Christian sense . . . The fruitfulness of a couple must be controlled by reason, by intelligence and by the spirit. It shall not be left to the exercise of automatic sex activity which is allowed free rein, any more than it shall be checked and curtailed as a nuisance. The power of a couple to be fertile must be given its highest possible significance through the fullest possible use of deliberate thinking. (Dr. Oraison)

Control of births may follow either of two procedures: the techniques of contraception, or the practice of continence.

Contraceptive devices are not without their dangers; their very multiplicity is proof that none of them is wholly effective (see Chapter VII). Their one advantage is that they require no effort and are therefore within the reach of all. But humanity cannot admit to being livestock! The peopling of the earth and the fecundity of each couple cannot be considered solely from the angle of economics. The harmony of a home is not based only on mutual good-will, compatibility and good love-making techniques. It is also love *and* procreation, intimacy *and* fruitfulness.

The use of contraceptives is defended as a way of avoiding pregnancy. In fact, however, the "civilization of contraception," as it is called by Father de Lestapis, does not dismiss with absolute sureness the "risk" of pregnancy, but presents other greater "risks" in the form of numerous social and individual disorders. These dangers and disturbances all arise from the basic fact that the aim of contraception is to turn the conjugal act, a display of love, *away* from its creative end by dissociating love from procreation.

In the first place, when the sexual function is stripped of its procreative ends it is reduced to the level of an erotic game and leads in fact to increased sexual licentiousness. The risk of pregnancy yields to the danger that woman will be considered and sought after only for her body as the source of voluptuous pleasure. Instead of establishing equality between both married partners, contraceptive practices create the most monstrous inequality by debasing

111

one human person to the degraded level of a thing used by the other person for sheer enjoyment.

In the second place, the denial of the "delicate bio-psychological complex of birth" (S. de Lestapis) robs sexuality of its ability to develop in adult fashion, making it regress to the pubertal stage. This has profound repercussions on the psychological and social patterns of behavior of the individual.

Finally, when sexuality is cut away "from its essential reference to procreation and becomes just a capacity for erotic sport, aberrant notions begin to prevail concerning the two sexes and resistance to sex inversions is lowered." [5]

The fundamental point, always to be kept in mind, is that *the whole human being is concerned in whatever concept of sexuality is adopted.* There can be no fully adequate solutions to sexual problems except those which take into account every dimension of man.

> Touching the mystery of man one never knows where will end the repercussions of violence done to his nature and his soul. Because he is endowed with intellect and free choice it is impossible to foresee the results of a deviative twist imposed on him as one might predict the deflection of a billiard ball to which English has been applied. Results always pass all the anticipations of the sorcerer's apprentice . . . This explains the delusion and failure of all efforts to solve the sex problem when the formulas used are just recipes of mixed technical devices applied to a fragmentary or secondary aspect of a complex reality.[6]

It does not mean that nothing can be done, but only that one must reject easy solutions in the form of cunning and deceitful gimmicks which too often degrade man's spiritual being.

The part of reason in the use and control of the sexual instinct consists in cultivating chastity and continence, that is to say the mastery over sexual need. The couple must be able to mute the cry of this need whenever they must or desire. Of course this calls for a tremendous effort in self-abnegation, but the practice of chastity has the immense advantage

> of basing the equilibrium of a married couple upon the deep biological and psychological substructures of human personality itself. . . . Whereas contraceptive practices do no more than mask the lack of balance, the exercise of continence, foreseen and prepared for in a proper program of earlier education, steers the individual to the attainment of genuine equilibrium in sexual matters. This kind of birth control fosters growth into adulthood, while the use of contraceptives only serves to perpetuate adolescence beyond its normal limits. (S. de Lestapis)

Love, sex and chastity

What has been said so far can be summarized in three propositions:

1. Contraceptive practices are antiphysiological, and seriously impair the bio-psychological equilibrium of sex relations. Moreover since they are not fool-

proof, their systematic dissemination in certain countries has not at all put an end to criminal abortions, but has had just the opposite effect. But criminal abortion is a moral offense deserving of absolute ban, except when medically necessary.

2. Decisions as to the number of children and the spacing of their birth should be the responsibility of parents according to their conscience. Concern about the proper education of the young must be given precedence over reproduction of the species.

3. The most valid solution of the problem of birth control, effective in all areas, but admittedly the most difficult, is self-control, exercised as a mastery of self in love and as a mutual respect of one person for the other. Neither husband nor wife can be egotistic, for sexual pleasure is not an end in itself.

Continence is therefore mandatory in married life. The two reasons considered earlier (periods of unavoidable separation, and the necessity of spaced births), valid though they may be, are negative, and assume the appearance of being external and vexing coercions. The real reasons for continence run much deeper. Instead of having the appearance of an interdiction leveled at the couple, or a barrier thrown across the path of their love, continence can and must become an affirmative invigoration and betterment of their love life.

It is a necessity of love itself. Without periods of con-

114

tinence, the conjugal act cannot be, as it should, that great moment of the meeting of hearts. Carnal union must never be allowed to become a habit like having something hot and soothing to drink before bedtime. Nothing is so harmful as a habit if one gives the word its full sense of a mechanical regularity. When habit prevails, the partner no longer is one whom we love with the best that is in us and with whom we want to unite in respect and love, but someone we use as an instrument. Love has a savor all its own, but a too easy acquiescence to instinct will dull the taste even though people are unaware of the dulling. In quite opposite manner, the spacing of the acts of intercourse may very well "join" the spouses instead of separating them, and do this equally as well as intercourse itself, provided spacing is something truly wanted, not imposed.

Intervals of continence are then needed and even indispensable to give higher value and constant renovation to the sexual act. Union in the flesh must of course be fully spontaneous, yet it should not spring from instinct alone; it ought to be the meeting of two beings intent on making the mutual gift of self rather than on allowing themselves to be drawn to each other by mere physical desire. Continence is an integral part of married love. It hearkens not only to the call of external constraints but also to the demands of love, demands which are found just as well in couples not subject to separations, nor to the necessities of birth control (since they are childless through sterility), as among couples who must face such external restraints.

To this extent, continence viewed as chastity serves love instead of stifling it.

The awareness of carnal desire

Continence is moreover a requisite for Christian living. It is not contempt for the flesh, but rather the sharp expression of a determination not to let the flesh deaden the sound of God's voice as it issues directives which make it easier for one person to better love another. Continence is one of the forms of the readiness of every Christian to do God's will.

Nevertheless it is equally true that continence, *of and by itself,* is harmful. If it is to bear good fruit it cannot remain just an abstention, for under this guise and considered as a pure and simple refusal, it leads to repression. Repression is heavily stressed by those who, in the name of hygiene, would like to reduce human sexuality to the animal level and therefore deny the possibility of an evolution toward spirituality.

Everyone has much to say about this repression; but what exactly is it? Repression is the subconscious rejection by the individual of certain tendencies which countersexuality (meaning moral, religious and social precept) shows him as reproachful. Repression does no more than transpose instinct, blacken it and make it a shameful force that casts evil and contaminating reflections over the mind. Sexual repression is a source of resentment, false idealism and hypocritical virtue.

The carnal reality of human love should not indeed be denied nor repressed. Repression has nothing to do with the exercise or the non-exercise of physical sexuality; it does imply that whereas sexual intercourse is set aside for some reason or other a certain erotic tension will be maintained, with consequent wishful thoughts about the suppressed sexual act. The continent individual, by definition, abstains from intercourse; but if at the same time he cultivates in his mind thoughts and imaginative fantasies whose erotic nature makes them equivalent to the normal preliminaries of the sexual act, he brings his genitals to a state of exasperation which gravely arouses his sexuality and leads to masturbation. At any rate the way is open to nervous disorders.

Although continence alone, as mere suppression, is contrary to our animal nature and harmful to health, it is *not so* when it is accompanied and qualified by chastity. Continence, if it be just the physical abstention from all sexual activity because of a moral or physical necessity that is bowed to rather than accepted, remains negative. Chastity on the contrary is not negative, not a deprivation, but an increment. It is a virtue, a positive energy of the mind. It is an attitude of the will which rejects, in thought and deed, forbidden sensual pleasures. These delights might not be prohibited in the same way for an adolescent, for an unmarried adult, for married couples or for someone, who in a given state of life, has declared a choice for absolute and definitive chastity. For each of these states of life chastity takes a special form. In marriage it consists in living the delights and joys of sexuality in accordance with what they mean and the purpose they were intended to serve, not in seeking these pleasures in themselves or for selfish ends.

It is therefore necessary that one learn how *not* to use sexuality in the way of an animal. This implies from the very first a complete and valid education in sexual things, to rule out any possibility of pathological repressions. Because continence is at once so difficult and so necessary, drills and exercises in it are a must. One has to learn how to be chaste and to acquire full growth through chastity. The dramatic problems of conscience which face so many couples and are so vexing as to cause at times the complete abandonment of all religious practice are traceable to the lack of spirit of self-sacrifice and generosity. A solid moral constitution has had to be built up in preparation for the encounter with those terrible difficulties of carnality; a preparation in depth through education in the meaning of love as described in these pages, and a more immediate preparation just prior to marriage. Care must be taken not to allow the start of habits which soon become inveterate and tyrannical, making the struggle more difficult and victory uncertain. The bondage of the flesh is a terrible one, and carnality soon becomes obsessive if one gives it free rein. Education in sex and love is needed to prevent the flesh from overpowering the spirit, to transform it instead into the special means of bringing about a union of hearts and souls.

It is quite natural that

> this requirement should seem superhuman, and its fulfillment out of the reach of those who live in spiritual mediocrity, ruled by selfishness instead of by love, in a soulless world where on the one hand conditions of living, work and housing are inconsistent with normal and sound family life, and on the other simultaneously an aphrodisiac civilization over-stimulates sex at every turn through promiscuousness, street solicitations, work conditions, crowding of transportation facilities, not to mention the hallucinating suggestiveness of the movies, the theater, television and a literature obsessed with sex." (Riquet)

What is needed above all is the conviction, reaching through the most intimate fibers of one's being, that chastity is of high value and that its place in married life is very important. Humanly it is unattainable, presenting, as it does, difficulties that are almost insurmountable. But in the light of real interior life and through wise use of prayer and the sacraments, in the supernatural climate of faith, hope and charity, chastity becomes, if not easy, at least possible. "Without me ye can do nothing."

The occasional practice of continence means a hard struggle. At such times we must remember that we win only those battles whose winning we are firmly convinced is an absolute necessity. Of course chastity will be made much easier to practice if couples are

> . . . sustained by the teachings, the backing and the many comfortings of a Christian community which creates and maintains conditions of life favorable to the flowering of virtues that make the complete performance of duty sufficiently easy. Other provisions are early training in chastity, mastery over sexuality, preparation for marriage, for motherhood, for the educative role of parents, as well as the adoption of social reforms that will ensure for the family—even the large family—conditions of living and housing really suitable to human beings. (Riquet)

All these factors greatly favor the practice of chastity as well as every other virtue, but they do not eliminate the need for personal effort. Each of us must try to put his finger on the sensitive points of his own specific weakness which is compounded with such variables as his education, social background, memories of sexual things and the quality of his emotional reaction to sex. Conditioned reflexes of a sexual nature are indeed very different according to individuals, racial groups and cultural settings. Each one of us must be able to look at himself and know himself clearly, sincerely and humbly enough to uncover and cleanse any dark corner of himself in which there might be a swarming of unavowable tendencies.

> The sex impulse . . . is generally aroused and, at any rate, becomes urgent *only* because of some external excitation of the sense of smell, of sight, of touch, or through the internal recall in our memory of some past impression of those senses. Sensory stimulations and mental pictures will inflame desire all the more as they are more vivid, concrete and graphically perceptible.[7]

120

Not only must we brush aside these excitations the moment they begin,, but we must avoid exposing ourselves foolishly to temptations which our own intimate experience has abundantly proved were not always easy to overcome. Anything likely to cause sexual stimulation through erotic thoughts and fancies *must* be shunned by one who wants to remain chaste. The name of the devil of sex is legion. To cite but two of his names, the most commonplace and current ones might be dancing and public entertainment, the movies in particular.

Dancing is admittedly a natural human activity and a real need of youth, as an expression of the joy of life. King David indeed danced before the Ark of the Covenant. A stupid ban on adolescent participation in dancing is therefore not in order. Yet it is true that dancing, of its very nature, tends to excite sexual desire; in primitive societies and in those that are in fact or fancy more developed, dancing is a normal prelude to sexual coupling. If therefore we are consciously aware that we love to dance, not for the pure joy of rhythmic motion but for the purpose of deriving sensuous pleasure in sexually unsound circumstances, it will be wise and prudent of us to avoid dancing, at least with some particular male or female partner who is especially exciting in a sexual way.

The same is true, *mutatis mutandis,* of going to the movies. So long as a film, even one which is open to criticism on moral grounds, attracts us solely by the values of its photography, or its theme and plot, our interest, far from being forbidden, is perfectly justifiable since this art

121

form is so particularly of our time. But from the moment we cultivate attendance at these film showings for the immediate purpose of seeking excitement in viewing the largely unveiled physical features of male and particularly female stars and of storing up a fund of sensual memories from which to draw later endless sexual excitement, then it is best to stay away from such filmed representations. This is what every spiritual adviser should always recommend to those in his charge.

It is indeed completely impossible to remain continent, or to avoid animalizing the conjugal act, if sexual desire is toyed with and allowed to be goaded and stimulated. The feeling that even when desire grows to lust it can still be quelled is always a false hope and a conceit. The only outcome would be a repression, and the real dangers of such a thing have been clearly underscored. It is easy to see that chastity means *prevention* much more than suppression.

> But this defensive attitude and this being on guard are the negative aspects of the struggle. Stopping at this would occasion nothing but enervating restlessness and depressing fatigue. All too often scruples and anxieties are fostered in this way, as well as other pathological and nervous disorders. Man was not made to avoid evil, but to do good; not to tear down, but to build, not to hate, but to love. Any human being who thinks only of protecting and preserving life botches life.[8]

Chastity must be loved and practiced as the way to a

greater and more beautiful mutual love. There is oneness as much in the jointly sustained effort as in the happiness lived through together. Love is purified and rid of the waste and the foibles that usually are its greater or lesser burden.

Married partners become more interdependent, more concerned about each other's difficulties, readier to lend a hand, as well as humbler in asking each other for help while confessing one's own perplexities. Thus everything moves in the direction of greater openheartedness, of mutual helpfulness, of wider assumption of responsibilities, in a word, of a more beautiful love. Practicing chastity and continence does not mean behaving like brother and sister, in restraint of every gesture of affection. Far from it: since the effort demands so much will power, will power in turn must receive the support and comfort of loving tenderness.

Chastity must be practiced out of the greater love for others. Continence is a sacrifice and therefore a mortification, but is also a redemption. We must be ready to offer this sacrifice not only as a purification of our own love, but also as a purification of the love of all those who love too little or badly, and as an atonement for all the defilements of the carnal union and of love itself.

And finally chastity must be practiced out of greater love for God. Intervals of continence will lead to God quite directly because they will make the partners love each other more while disposing them to be more obedient to God in greater readiness to do His will, and to be therefore less self-centered and self-seeking. Their union with God will be direct because they will find themselves in a way driven to prayer as a last resort, to call upon the special grace of their sacrament for the help they need to "take it," not only in overcoming the hardship of continence, but also in transforming it into a thing of beauty, into a transfiguration of their love.

* * *

The positive side of chastity needed to be boldly stressed in order to bring out the essential fact that contrary to general belief neither chastity nor virginity have any value in themselves. If they had, it would be a matter of non-sexuality, which is their very opposite, as it would mean the negation of love, if we are to take this word in its full significance of something tied in with emotional life. What worth they have comes "only from the dedication in which they start, continue, grow and acquire spiritual significance. They have value to the exact degree that they are placed, like love, in the service of others. Their value is not that they are a refusal of human love, but that they establish the conditions of access to higher love according to each person's particular state in life." [9] "If things are not so, chastity and continence are in danger of being a simple repudiation of the [marriage] promise and a mutilation." [10]

The powers of chastity and continence must not be left

untapped but must be made productive by shifting their point of application, namely, by directing them toward superior ends. If the individual accepts the curbing of sexuality as something good for his spiritual self, if he can transcend egotism and manage to use chastity in the service of an ideal, then "sublimation" is attained, the very opposite of repression, the former being fruitful and oriented toward others, the latter being barren and twisted back upon the self.

Chastity conceived as a sublimation is not only possible, but is widely practiced as such. All around us there are men and women who are not only "normal" but superior, perfectly balanced in every respect, capable of sustained and effective endeavors of mind and body; they live out their single lives by choice and will, standing out as magnificent exemplars of humanity; the men do not fall into sissiness, which would make them dull and colorless, nor do the women grow mannish in a denial of their femininity. Science, art, politics, social work, military careers or religious dedication are many fields among others that can polarize and engross the instinctive and emotional powers of a human being, allowing for freedom and effectiveness of action in a rarely equalled degree, without trace of physical or psychological withering, nor moral warping.

If married love is the field in which the human person elects to seek its growth, then the only avenue to complete flowering is the gift of self. Selfish pursuit of pleasure

125

falls far short of paying off in human values and deep joy to the same degree as do devotion and sacrifice to a cause. Even

> from the purely biological point of view it seems that the internal secretions of the sexual glands, whose activity is of such importance to the full growth of a man or a woman, are provoked less through the expending of nervous energy in the performance itself of the physical act of intercourse, than by the love which, potentially or actually, results from the act. Sexual life, a relation conditioned by someone outside ourself, and therefore not dependent on our will alone, is no more necessary, strictly speaking, to our balance or our full development than are any other sensory activities, like the function of sight, for example . . . Enforced sexual inactivity or lack of conjugal relations still leaves both husband and wife, father or mother, free to orient their lives toward other fulfillments which marriage would have ruled out.[11]

In all instances and in every way it is love, with the true gift of self, which ennobles our personality and gives meaning to our life and our endeavors.

IV

Understanding the Pleasure of Sex

The first part of this study has led progressively to some intimate acquaintance with the mystery of human love. It is our hope that it has been objective enough. We trust it has avoided the three pitfalls to which studies of its kind are exposed, namely pornography, sentimentality and narrow bigotry.

Attempting now to summarize in concrete form the essential points of its exposition, let us say that the love of man and woman can be represented in the form of a pyramid with four sides, a base and a summit.

The first side is physical love; that hormonal urge, in-

127

stinctive and brutal, which affects us in the most defenseless and least well-known area of our being. We subject ourselves to the age-old law which drives every living organism to attempt to perpetuate itself through its own offspring. It consists in the physical climax occasioned by a shock and a commotion affecting every fiber in us.

The second side of the pyramid is emotional love. Sexual relations in mankind, even the most degraded ones, always retain at least a slight glimmer of the divine spark which was struck one day in the first man and woman and has since made them and their descendants radically different from animals.

Human love, while it *is* instinct and to the *extent* it is instinct, is also a probing, in company with a partner mysteriously chosen from among all others, of the need for infinity which is felt so insistently by every human creature. The very meeting with this partner of the opposite sex brings about a fullness of joy that is equal in its own way to the unreserved carnal embraces normally due to follow. Bonded in this mysterious and exclusive emotion, and having found in it what was needed to give human nature its total integration, the human couple becomes self-sufficient. "Lovers are alone in the world. Nothing exists, nothing can exist, nothing has any real value outside the one I love. The universe is in those eyes, in that smile, in that face which I can really call mine because I love it, and because my love is returned. Everything is subordinate to our love which is out of time and out of space. It exists, and all else is lost in the mist."

The third side of the pyramid is the sociological aspect of love. This is a matter first of the nature of the relations between the interested parties themselves. Human love relations head the list of interpersonal relationships; they demand respect for the two individualities concerned, and even more than respect, the assurance that one person will help the other grow to full human stature. Marriage must allow each partner to realize his or her own deep potentialities, to become his or her own self. But furthermore the sociological side of human love concerns, by extension, the offspring of this love, the children; it should extend even further, to the role which the married couple plays in the society of men. Much more could be said on this subject, but that would be digressing from the immediate topic of this present book.

The fourth side of the pyramid represents the spiritual aspect of love. Love is not alone a form of enjoyment, not alone the search by man or woman for an indispensable complement, not alone the most intimate and thorough of interpersonal relations; it is also the very special means of sharing in a progressive humanization of mankind. In other words, the distance separating man from beast is measurable in terms of the concept which men and their society have concerning love. For although no biological break exists between us and animals, there is indeed a real chasm between them and us with respect to the disposition of the nervous system and the potentialities of permanent control which this arrangement allows the brain to exercise over the impulses of instinct. Consequently, if humanity wants to maintain its higher station, transcending animality, it must chart its course of progress towards greater and greater spirituality.

All four sides of our pyramid rest upon its one common base, which must be taken to represent human nature; neither flesh alone, nor pure spirit, but forever a mixture of spirit and flesh. The various components of love find their reason for existing and their justification in this combination of matter and mind whose balance is unstable, and constantly threatened and questioned. It is man's dreadful distinction that he must be subjected to a multitude of tendencies, impulses, instincts and even secretions, and, in the midst of them, stay bound in duty to become and remain his own human self, by the never-ending effort of his free will.

He will never really assert his human personality short of sidestepping the snares of the mind, for one thing, and also shaking off the shackles of matter. He must make use of both mind and matter in his climb to the summit of the triangle, in an indispensable conquest that will translate the inborn yearnings of every human being for a world of love, free from temptations and aberrations, purified by the spirit, but still a solid part of the four sides and base of the period.

* * *

It would be pretentious to claim that this subject has been exhaustively treated. The intent of this first part, to state it very modestly, was to clarify, and especially to put in their proper place and rank, all things having to do with human love. Some readers may now have a clearer insight with regard to themselves, and find the solution to some of their problems by reflecting upon one passage or another. But others may still need further outside assistance. To these we say "Be of good heart"! It is unheard of that any person of good will, searching and struggling, shall not some day find the key to the secret lock of the door that opens on peace and serenity.

PART TWO

The Physical Aspects of Love

V

Sex and the Human Anatomy

The male genital system

Essentially the male genital system is composed of the following parts.

A) *Two principal glands called testes or testicles,* located outside the abdominal cavity controlled by two distinct cell groups: (1) an internal secretion of an endocrine gland called the male hormone or *testosterone,* which is responsible for the secondary sex characteristics of the male, such as the muscular development, low pitched

135

voice, hair distribution, etc.; (2) an external secretion of male reproductive cells or *spermatozoa* which are produced by the seminiferous (seed-bearing) tubules of the testis. These tubes extend into the *epididymis,* an oblong body composed of the convoluted efferent duct of the testis, at the posterior part of that organ leading to the deferent canal.

B) The *deferent canal* or *vas deferens,* the duct which enters the abdomen, passes behind the bladder and carries the spermatozoa on their way to the penis through the seminal vesicles or tubes described below. The vas deferens is accompanied by veins and nerves to and from the testicle.

C) The *seminal vesicles,* two membranous, secculated tubes situated at the base of the bladder, serving as receptacles to which the semen gathers during the intervals that separate ejaculations. They also contain tiny glands which secrete the seminal liquid. Each seminal vesicle is branched to each deferent canal, and the junction of the seminal duct with the deferent canal constitutes the *ejaculator duct,* a very short body located in the prostate gland and opening into the urethra.

D) The *urethra* is the genito-urinary duct which extends from the bladder through the length of the penis to its very tip or *glans.* In its posterior section, after going through the prostate, it is surrounded by the *striate sphincter,* a ring of muscular tissue which serves to close the tubular passage. The floor of the urethra, as it passes within

136

the prostate gland, is marked with a ridge or crest of erectible tissue called the *verumontanum,* which swells at the moment of erection of the penis, and along with the closing action of the sphincter prevents both the passing down of urine and the upward passage of semen toward the bladder.

E) The *prostate* is a gland the size of a chestnut located at the base of the bladder around the urethra. Its cells are grouped in clusters, like grapes (an arrangement described as *racemose*) and produce a secretion called the *prostatic fluid* which contributes to the vitality of the spermatozoa. One might say that this point is like a crossroads of the genito-urinary system, comprising the prostate gland itself, the urethra, the terminal point of the deferent canal, the seminal vesicles and the ejaculatory ducts. It is the converging point of all the glandular secretions which make up the semen. Specifically, the contractions of the prostate help propel the semen towards the penis, while at the same time, by blocking the urethra, they prevent urine from mixing with the seminal fluid.

F) The *penis* is the copulative male organ. Habitually cylindrical in shape, it hangs anteriorly to the scrotum. During erection it swells, increases in volume, becomes rigid and rises in front of the abdomen. It terminates in a cone-shaped bulge, the *glans,* in which there is a large concentration of nerve ends, and which is more or less completely enclosed, in time of repose, within a wrapping of loose skin called the *prepuce* or *foreskin.*

Essentially the penis is made up of erectile tissues known as *corpora cavernosa* (two in number) and one *corpus spongiosum*. These are highly vascular and capable of being distended and made rigid when distended with blood, reaching a state known as *erection*.

G) The *semen* is the fluid produced by the generative organs of the male. An extremely complex chemical compound, it consists of two parts: one which is secreted by the testicles and is highly fertile, containing as it does innumerable spermatozoa. The other, sterile in itself, contains the elements necessary for the vitality of the spermatozoa. It is produced in the accessory glands described above: seminiferous vesicles, urethral and prostate glands, etc.

An ejaculation of semen averages 3.39 milliliters in volume, but this is subject to great variation in the same individual. The volume decreases when there is repeated intercourse, but may increase to as much as 13 milliliters, after a long period of continence. It would seem necessary, however, that the volume of the ejection stay within normal limits, so that on the one hand the acidity of vaginal secretions may be neutralized; and on the other hand, so that fertility may not be impaired by excessive dilution of the sperm.

At the moment of ejaculation there first appears a droplet or two of colorless fluid intended to neutralize the acid condition of the urethral duct prior to the passage of the ejaculation itself. Next comes the milky prostatic secretion which contains no spermatozoa. Then there follows that part of the seminal fluid which bears the spermatozoa, and finally the secretion of the seminal vesicles, a highly viscous, jelly-like and starchy fluid resembling tapioca.

The sperm content of semen ranges between 100 to 225 million spermatozoa per cubic centimeter, with 20 million representing the lowest level of fertility. This concentration varies to a great degree in one and the same person. Intense emotional excitement and muscular fatigue have a negative effect; extended continence, as well as a rise in the temperature within the testes also tend to lower the proportion of spermatozoa in the seminal ejaculation.

The faculty which spermatozoa have of moving about increases and can be maintained even in artificial surroundings and at ordinary temperatures for periods of from three to five hours; but in the natural ambiance of the woman's vagina this motility lasts much longer because the germ-cells find there the substances which their metabolism requires. Heat increases motility of the spermatozoa, but reduces their span of life.

The female genital system

Essentially it is divided into the five following parts.

A) Two *ovaries*, each of which is situated in the upper region and on either side of the true pelvis. Both ovaries perform a twofold function:

—the internal secretion of the female hormones, called *estrogens* and *progesterone*. Estrogens are responsible for woman's secondary sexual characteristics: a pelvis which is more widely flared than man's, longer and more abundant hair, larger breasts, high-pitched voice, distribution of body hairs, etc. Progesterone is the hormone that sets the stage for pregnancy by preparing the female organism to receive the fertilized ovum;—an external secretion, the as yet unfertilized female reproductive cell, the ovum or egg.

B) The *Fallopian tubes*, bilateral and symmetrical passages, one of each in contact with each ovary, and designed to convey the ovum from the ovary to the uterus.

C) The *uterus* or womb, a hollow, muscular organ of two parts, the body or *fundus,* and the neck or *cervix.* Its role is to receive the ovum, retain and protect it, allow it to develop into a *fetus,* and then expel it at birth.

D) The *vagina*, is a tubular passage extending from the neck of the womb down to the vulva. It is the female organ of copulation.

E) The *vulva*, or entrance, is the external opening of the female genital organs and is comprised of all the external parts of the female genital system. The vulva has a midway depression into which open the urethra and the vagina; the lower part of the vagina is separated from the vulva by a thin membrane, more or less completely closed in a virgin, called the *hymen.*

Each side of the vulva is lined by a double fold of mucocutaneous tissue, the external folds being called *labia majora* or larger lips, and the internal folds *labia minora*, or smaller lips. The labia minora are attached at their forward extremities to an erectile organ, the *clitoris,* which corresponds with the male's penis; erection of the clitoris, though much less pronounced than that of its male homolog, plays a supremely important part in harmonious intercourse. It is, like the glans of the penis, very abundantly supplied with nerve endings, and is the principal, even the sole, center of sensuous pleasure in the younger woman.

How the hormones operate

At the lower levels of life, beings have no sex. One cell divides into two which are identically the same as the first, and so on. Sexed reproduction appears only at a later stage in animal evolution and constitutes a tremendous forward step, consisting as it does in the fusion of two specialized cells, sprung from two different beings and giving birth to an entirely different individual endowed with a personality and an originality that are totally distinct from those of its progenitors.

The reproductive cells are produced by the sexual glands whose development, from birth onward, is assured in turn by other glands furnishing internal secretions, or endocrines, thus called because these chemical secretions, named *hormones,* pass directly into the blood and act on other glands. The sexual glands themselves become endocrines the moment they outgrow the infant stage, reach their maturity and are ready to function. It is their secretions, the sexual hormones, that will condition sexual development as well as emotional balance in each individual human being.

> It has been said of adult hormonal secretions in the aggregate that they form a concert: the word perfectly points up at once the harmonies existing between them, and the balances that require continual readjustments. The most recent discoveries show also the correlations that exist between hormones and the nervous equipment of vegetative life as this equipment attends to the processes of metabolism or general nutrition. Thanks to research done within the past half-century, the sex hormones, which are normally in the limelight from puberty to senescence, have been given firm rank among those most highly active substances which make of every living being a complex whole, composed of parts that are quite unlike one another yet are coordinated with, integrated into, and subordinated to the whole: an individual different from all others, identifiable to himself at all times, yet changing at every moment along the curve of his own personality.[1]

A human being is an aggregate incapable of being dissociated. Sex influences its organism as a whole, and not one function of that organism singly escapes the sway of sexuality because the sexual hormones are carried in the blood stream through the entire body and act in a specific way upon each and every organ. They intervene in every phase of nutrition, impregnating the entire nervous system, the nervous centers of vegetative life, or relational life, of the spine and the brain. Every part of the body can be said to be sexualized, even eroticized, by the sex hormones.

Their influence is exercised particularly on the following areas: (1) on the *lower* or *medullary* nerve centers, so called because they abide near the base of the spinal cord and are responsible for the very complex automatic reflexes which are elicited during sexual intercourse; and (2) on the *higher* nerve centers, so designated because they are located in the brain, where they are the hub and seat of the essentially human activities of intelligence, will, etc. Because they are constantly permeated with sex hormones, they yield and react to the hormonal influence that is specific to each sex, and this gives the intellect, the sensibility, the emotional affectibility and the will of each sex the coloring and the key peculiarly and properly its own.

The nervous system, and notably the brain, on the other hand, exercises upon the whole organism—and therefore upon the sexual functions—a power of command, restraint and control which intervenes to discipline and direct generative life.

* * *

The man's sexual activity assumes two forms. The first is the production of an external secretion, intended to be expelled from the organism, and consisting of the *semen*, a complex fluid described earlier as containing in suspension millions of fertilizing cells, the spermatozoa or sperm. The second form is the production of an internal secretion, *testosterone*, the male sexual hormone.

These two kinds of secretions can perfectly well be dissociated; lack of semen makes a man sterile, lack of hormones makes him impotent. It must be noted that a man's impotence is generally of psychological origin, and that conversely, proper psychical disposition may compensate at times for hormonal deficiencies.

Both forms of testicular activity just now described are influenced by an endocrine or ductless gland attached to the base of the brain, the *hypophysis* or *pituitary gland*. Its anterior part secretes two hormones which are called *gonado trophins* because their mission is to stimulate the activity of the *gonads* or sexual glands, namely the testicles. These two gonado trophins cause respectively the production of hormones and the production of the spermatozoa which were mentioned earlier.

Genital activity in the man does not so abruptly change as it does in the woman at menopause. It goes on for a much longer time, and its abatement is always gradual. Neither are there any sudden alterations in the functioning of the testes between the ages of forty and eighty. The loss of sexual potency is always slow and gradual, with individual variations. Moreover, senescence is not under the exclusive dependence of the sexual glands, which degenerate along with the rest of the organism, yet frequently retain their activity for a longer time than some of the other organs.

* * *

If the man's hormonal functioning is remarkably simple, regular and constant, its counterpart in the woman is definitely not so. From puberty to menopause, woman is subject to the relentless successions of ovulations and menses, with relief coming only during pregnancies and at the time of breast-feeding. This hormonal biphasic rhythm causes a general and endocrine unevenness generally every twenty-eight days. Congestion of the uterus and of its accessory organs reoccurs periodically, and the rhythmical activity of the ovaries, carrying along with it secretions of every other gland of the organism, causes alternative engorging and discharge of the various hormonal secretions as the monthly cycle progresses through its modifications. Dovetailing this pattern of constant commotion of incessant ebb and flow within the female organism, the character traits of a woman have parallel contours of variability, emotionalism, instability, impulsiveness and intuition. All those traits are marked more deeply in a woman than a man because the broken hormonal rhythm of her genital functions responds with deep pulsations upon her emotional life.

The events that take place from one menstrual period to the next are known in the aggregate as the *menstrual cycle*.

Its duration, varying from one woman to another, and in each woman from time to time, is generally of twenty-eight days, not thirty or thirty-one as is often believed.

In the simplest of outlines, one may describe the phenomena of this cycle as follows, dividing them into four phases and agreeing that the first day of the entire cycle shall be the one on which the flow of blood begins.

A) The first, or estrogenic, phase lasts until the fourteenth day. In its course, the pituitary gland secretes a hormone, similar to the male hormone of the same name. This first secretion is specifically called *folliculostimuline,* or F.S.H. for short. It triggers the development of an ovarian follicle, or ovisac (the Graafian follicle). This cell produces the first female sexual hormone, estrogen. This hormone, in turn, is discharged into the blood and induces a process of rebuilding and thickening of the mucous membrane of the uterus which had been shed during the preceding menses. Simultaneously, the secretion of F.S.H. is arrested and the pituitary body begins to generate a second gonado trophin, luteinizing hormone, or L.H.

B) The second phase or period is *ovulation.* When both hormones, F.S.H. and L.H., reach a certain point of balance, the regular process of formation and discharge of the ovum begins, generally midway in the whole cycle, i.e., on the fourteenth day. The ovarian follicle, has reached full development, its wall bulging the surface of the ovary; it breaks open, releasing the ovum which is at once gathered into the Fallopian tube, to proceed

146

thereafter through this duct down to the cavity of the uterus.

C) Now begins the *luteal* phase which will last until the next menstrual period. Estrogen continues to be secreted, but the ruptured follicle is converted into a yellowish structure called the *corpus luteum,* whose short-lived existence depends on the luteotrophic hormone (L.T.H.) *Progesterone,* which was classified earlier as the second of the two principal female sex hormones is secreted by the corpus luteum. It also influences the lining of the uterus to secrete nourishment for the egg if it happens to have been fertilized and to remain there.

D) The final phase is specifically called *menstruation.* When fertilization does not occur, the corpus luteum degenerates in its turn. The level of the ovarian hormones in the blood drops abruptly, resulting in a sudden elimination of the uterine mucous membrane; the blood vessels of the uterus are opened and they bleed. This is menstruation, the menstrual flow, the menses. And once again the secretion of the hormone folliculostimuline begins.

This bare outline calls for a few thoughts and remarks.

1. From the outset one is struck by the intricacy of a mechanism that requires the interplay of so many self-regulating systems. Modern research in cybernetics, the science dealing with the mechanics of communication and control in living organisms and machines, has shed new light upon the workings of the female hormonal system, allowing us at least to perceive the necessity for perfect

concordance and the combined action, between the pituitary gland and the ovaries.

But things are far more complicated than just that, for the pituitary body itself is dependent to a degree on an extremely delicate nerve center, the *hypothalamus,* which is highly responsive to excitations of all kinds: humoral, nervous, psychological, emotional, even climatic. It is through this sensitive nerve center that the factors just mentioned may cause disturbances in the menstrual cycle.

2. Although ovulation and menstruation are both part of the one cycle, they are quite distinct. In the course of a strictly normal cycle they are perfectly co-ordinated. But there may be the cycles without ovulation yet with no change in the timing of the menses.

3. A woman cannot be fecundated or impregnated at just any moment of the cycle. The ovule has a rather short span of life: it is able to be fertilized only within a period of no more than twenty-four hours following its release from the ovary. For their part, the spermatozoa retain their potency for a longer time, approximately two days. Thus, fertilization or fecundation, the meeting and fusion of the two gametes, ovum and sperm, is able to take place only during a brief period, to be precise during *the two or three days that precede ovulation, and during the twenty-four to forty-eight hours following it.* The problem therefore of achieving or avoiding pregnancy lies in determining as exactly as possible the date ovulation takes place.

4. It is towards the end of the first, or folliculinic, phase and at the moment of ovulation (except in cases of painful ovulation) that a woman is at her seductive, vivacious and playful best, and it is then that she most wants sexual relations. There is logic to this, since anatomy tells us that it is the very time when fertilization is possible. But in quite opposite a fashion, as menstruation approaches, she is beset with physical discomforts and mental discontents in mournful procession. Her face is drawn, reddened; she has pains and swelling in the lower abdomen; her legs hurt and she feels exhausted, etc. All this is reflected in her disposition, for she becomes nervous and tense, touchy, impressionable, dispirited and discouraged. Young husbands must know how to read these signs, understand their significance, and give every proof of gentleness, comprehension and patience.

5. Finally—and this thought transcends the lower levels of mere anatomy—one cannot fail to be impressed by the complemental quality of the sexual systems of each sex. Either of them, male or female, is incomplete in isolation from the other and therefore useless. By itself, each is only half of a system. The union of these parts is what gives them meaning and totality. "Biologically, sex makes sense only in togetherness." (Norman) Again, one is struck by the capital differences between the sexes. In one the genital system is outward, obvious, aggressive, brutally conquering; in the other, everything is delicate, undisplayed, gentle, receptive. In the male, the sexual func-

tions operate smoothly, without complications; in the female there occur sudden, periodic interruptions in the hormonal rhythm with deep repercussions throughout the physical organism. The psychological framework is also deeply affected. One sex is impulsive, the other reserved; one conquers, the other is conquered; one has blunt desires that are instantly revealed by exterior manifestations, while in the other, similar yearnings are much more subtle, requiring time to adapt before they can be expressed. One is very quickly and powerfully solicited by an instinct whose satisfaction brings him immediate, lusty and turbulent pleasure, while for the other the entire sexual system has meant, from puberty onwards, nothing but annoyance and sometimes even pain. For a man, the sexual act occurs outside his body, but for a woman it is internal; the man's physical integrity suffers no impairment, but the woman's body is not only hurt from the inception of intercourse (because of defloration) but will undergo physical deformation, great discomfort and suffering if the sexual act is followed by its normal consequence, pregnancy. Man finds release and independence after intercourse, but woman knows that each time she is pledging her future; man is free to think of no one but himself, while woman cannot allow herself not to think of the child.

How the sexual act affects the mind and body

"Sex instinct is a primordial tendency which drives men and woman to seek particular voluptuous sensations." (A. Binet) Sex instinct is different and distinct from the reproductive instinct, although in many cases both these independent drives may combine, as they often do particularly in woman. The sex instinct is an impulse towards sexual union leading to the voluptuous climax of physical love. Physiologically, climax comes about through an aggregate of organic, reflex reactions that result from the stimulation of nervous centers of extremely complex nature. These are going to be described in the following pages.

What are the sexual stimulants?

Sexual reflexes are set in motion by a number of stimuli which awaken sex desire by making more objective and perceptible the normal attraction one sex has for the other. These stimuli are of three kinds.

A) *External or sensory stimuli:*
Every one of the senses has an array of sensations to offer.

1. *Sight:* in the human species this sense is the first to

enter into play in stimulating sexual desire. Its role is decisive for through sight is derived the concept of beauty, an ideation whose importance is of the highest order, particularly to a man; in a woman's eyes physical beauty as such is secondary to the impression she gets visually of a male's manly bearing, his look of importance or the magnetism of his personality.

2. *Hearing:* a woman is far more responsive than a man to auditory impression. The timbre, or tone quality of a certain masculine voice is an unrivalled enticement for a woman, and many a practiced seducer owes to it the best of his success. Furthermore, speech can lull reason, soothe and mesmerize, and women of all times and climes ask and demand of their lover, of their husband that he speak words, the same but the ever new words which they want to hear, "Tell me that you love me!"

3. *Senses of smell and taste:* in most animal species the sense of smell is of cardinal importance to sexuality, but its role in humans is only secondary, coming into play only after the sense of sight. Perfume and body scent may cause either attraction or revulsion, and a woman is much less disposed to be sensitive to them than a man. As for taste, the most selfish of all the senses, it has very little to do with sexuality.

4. *Sense of touch:* the determinant factor in sensory stimulation is the sense of touch, since physical love is composed mostly, and at times exclusively, of tactile feel-

ings and impressions. This is why Pierre Louÿs can speak, in his *Aphrodite,* about the "twenty-four parts of the body where caresses are irresistible." Of course, the other senses have blazed the trail by making the individual receptive, but the stimulation they give does not of itself too often culminate in sensuous climax.

B) *Internal stimuli:*

1. Nerve centers are made especially receptive to sexual excitation by inner sensations of well-being or euphoria induced by such things as a general feeling of good health, the slight headiness of sea or mountain air, or the first level of intoxication with alcohol which blunts the control of the will.

2. Sensations originating in the region of the pelvis are sufficient of themselves to stir the sex impulse. Anything that causes an accumulation of blood in the area of the genitals, thereby creating congestion and turgidness of the erectile sex organs, mechanically induces the first phase of sensual pleasure. Stimuli of this kind may be distension of the bladder, vibrations, or the well-fed feeling after a good meal.

C) *Psychological stimuli:*

Purely psychic representations can make up for the lack of external or internal physical stimulation. A thought, an erotic memory, anything that can stir the imagination is enough at times to set off genital activity.

Even emotions of a painful nature may do this, as in

153

the case of a woman who is upset by fear and for that reason gives herself more readily. On the other hand, other emotional reactions, like disgust, can suddenly quell sexual impulse.

The awareness of sexual excitement

Impressions that begin in the organs of sensory perception (eyes, ears, nose, etc.) are routed directly to the brain via the sensory nerves: optic, auditory and olfactory. Tactile sensations follow a more roundabout circuit, most of them reaching the brain after being relayed through the spinal cord. Deep sensations that start in the internal organs also use the relay from the spine to the brain. Psychic impressions of erotic nature occur immediately within the brain and provoke erection without any preamble of sensory or visceral excitation.

In a word, conscious perception of sexual excitement takes place in the brain, and there also emotional reaction to it develops and grows. The spinal centers co-ordinate all the processes of nerve centers and glands in an automated sequence that leads to the voluptuous climax. Actually it is very fortunate that the brain does control the nerve centers with a kind of braking action, for if the automatism of the spinal centers were allowed to run free, the state of erection and sexual tension might be mankind's quasi-continuous condition.

The intensity of sexual emotions

Sexual emotion causes organic reactions of greater or lesser intensity according to the individual persons affected, but the general pattern of these reflexes is common to every human being, man or woman, and it composes what has been called the "curve of sensual delight," comprising three phases:

1. The phase of *tumescence,* which might be represented as the rising of the curve. It begins with the preliminary stages of sexual excitation, and its name describes the swelling of the erectile sex organs.

2. The phase of *sensual paroxysm* or sexual climax marking the peak of the curve and called the *orgasm.*

3. The phase of *detumescence,* the descending part of the curve, during which the swelling of the organs of erection subsides, muscular and nervous tension is relaxed. In this phase a feeling of relief and general well-being invites the whole body to rest.

Instinctive love, physical love, love considered strictly from the physiological point of view is a motor reaction of very high intensity, but of very short duration, a "flashing" sensation. Maurice Barrès called it "the little jolt— *la petite sécousse."* And Marcus Aurelius described it as *"epilepsia brevis*—a short convulsion." Paul Valéry's wistful comment was, "When all is said and done, life's moment of greatest account is brief."

In the majority of animals and sometimes among humans, love does not go above that level: once the act is done, they separate and forget. Octave Béliard, speaking of animals, says of them, "those splendidly cynical beasts whose sex, generously satisfied in the face of the heavens, leaves them so untroubled."

Now for a closer and separate study of each of these three phases of organic reaction in a man, and in a woman.

Reactions of the male organs

A) *The preliminary phase.*

This is the warming-up period of early excitation, indispensable to the creating of a favorable relation between the partners and to proper conditioning of each one for the sexual act. It is characterized by a pattern of sensory or psychosensory reflexes incited by the woman's presence and nearness.

The reflexes are intended first to create in the man the *need* to have intercourse with this particular woman, and secondly to enable him to satisfy this need by causing the reactions that bring about erection. The closeness of the woman he desires puts man's psyche in a state of elation, of sensorial receptiveness, and builds up a flood of sexual impulses and needs which every one of his senses concurs in feeding. As was pointed out, sight and touch are the senses primarily involved in a human being, but the senses of smell and hearing are not by any means unconcerned. Simultaneously, the appetite of the whole nervous system is whetted by an increased production of hormones. The final outcome of this entire process of stimulation is to create and then progressively build up the erotic tension of sexual desire and need. The individual is set little by little to make the moves of sexual intercourse and to induce his wife to take part in it. All this is automatic and identical in all individuals, and the will is not responsible for any of these reflexes and reactions.

The localized expression of over-activity in the genital glands is seen in the phenomenon of *erection,* a reflex action under the command of a nerve center of the lower spinal cord. The penis was described earlier as having, throughout its length, the *corpus spongiosum* and the *corpora cavernosa,* whose Latin names are picturesque enough to suggest their mode of operation: under the influence of external and internal stimuli, these bodies distended with blood, dilate, and thus cause the penis to increase in size, protrude and become firm.

It should be remembered that during this entire first phase the erectile bodies are stimulated by two kinds of excitants: (1) tactile stimuli arising in the glans, transmitted to the spine through the pudendal nerve; and (2) stimuli originating in the brain which are relayed by the spine and the neuro-vegetative nerves. After the penis has penetrated the vagina, erection persists, but the course of the reflexes which maintain it is changed.

Erection is not the only localized modification of the organism to occur at this time. It is accompanied by a general increase of glandular activity; one manifestation of this is the appearance at the meatus (the opening of the penis) of a mucous-like secretion whose purpose is to lubricate the tip of the penis, neutralize the acidity of any remnants of urine or vaginal fluids and thereby, in concurrence with the prostatic liquid, help the vitality of the spermatozoa.

Activity of the testicles, which normally persists at all times, greatly increases at this moment. The seminal vesicles become filled with spermatozoa bathed in the seminal fluid which the vesicles generate.

In tune with the intense congestion or tumescence localized in the genitals, a number of more general reactions take place. The pace of the heartbeat and the rhythm of respiration accelerate, blood flows to the face, blood pressure rises, etc., in response to the increased flow of genital sex hormones.

The subject perceives all these sensations. While they are generally of pleasurable quality, they are also accompanied by a feeling of discomfort, fullness, and an impression of a lack of satisfaction. This very special condition makes discharge a need and calls for complete penetration as the only means of reaching the climax of

158

sensual pleasure and consequent relief. The pitch of eroticism reaches its high point at the end of this phase whose duration varies according to age, or depending on the partner.

B) *The sexual act itself: copulation.*

This second phase is essentially muscular. Immediately upon penetration, the back-and-forth movements of copulation are begun. Their function is to have erection persist and also to cause a greater charge and increase of nervous tension and sensuous pleasure in a cumulative rise to the orgasm. "It is as though each stroke of the glans along the sides of the vagina sent on to the centers . . . a wave of nervous influx gradually building up a charge of nervous energy." [2]

Although the tempo of the copulative movements can be changed at will, they are mostly reflex and involuntary. The tension which they build up in the nervous system, in function of their speed and reiteration, reaches its full measure more or less rapidly accordingly to the individuals involved; for some the threshold of orgasm and ejaculation is reached after just a few movements, while for others vaginal contact may be extended indefinitely.

Sensations of erotic pleasure which are latent in all sexual manifestations now assume a well-defined and localized character. "Following penetration, they are continuous, increasing with the rubbing movements and in proportion to their duration, repetition and intensity; the sensations are part of the phenomena of the nervous charge and they follow its progress. Beyond a certain point they become a kind of ecstatic climax which is called the orgasm." [3]

The *orgasm* is characterized by the intensification of all the objective and perceivable changes which ran before it in localized areas of the body as well as in the organism generally, and which involved circulatory, excretory, muscular and vasomotor activity. The copulative movements themselves are unconsciously made more sweeping and frequent, then are stopped abruptly. It should be noted that the orgasm is not always the same in one and the same individual, that its intensity depends neither on the degree nor the duration of the erection, and that it sometimes occurs before the start of any copulative movements.

Ejaculation is a reflex action consisting in the expulsion of the seminal fluid in successive, spasmodic and decreasing spurts.

In the first phase, the genital reservoirs—sac of the vas deferens, seminal vesicles, urethral glands and prostate— are emptied by a contraction of their walls into the posterior part of the urethra. In the second phase, the urethra contracts, but evacuation is hindered by the spasm of a ring of muscle. As tension increases inside the urethra the muscle spasm yields, and part of the seminal fluid is expelled. As a result tension is relieved and the muscular contraction is repeated; but this renewed contraction causes tension to increase again; the muscle spasm yields a second time, more semen is expelled, and then the entire cycle is repeated over and over until complete expulsion of the semen.

C) *The phase of detumescence.*

This last phase is marked by a sense of fatigue, as would happen after any other muscular and nervous exertion. This tired feeling goes along for a varying period of time, with loss of ability for excitation, abatement of desire, loss of the erection—which cannot readily be renewed— and retarded ejaculation. There is also drowsiness and sometimes, though not always, anguish, sadness and even revulsion against the partner. This period of being tired out varies in duration with the age of the subject; it is very short for younger men, but may last minutes or hours for those who have reached or passed adult maturity.

Note that the erotic tension, which is thus relaxed by the orgasm, still persists to some degree. There seems to remain some unused sensual pleasure, to be felt for a time lapse that is different in this or that individual, a few hours or several days. Further intercourse is often easier on the day after coitus that it is after several days. The individual indeed then reaches more readily his maximum excitation because he is already sensitized.

General opinion notwithstanding, abstention from any contact with a woman does not always allow an accumulation of the elements which compose the sex urge, though such a storing up may be possible in very young men. In older men just the opposite happens. Abstinence banks the genital fires and may cause the gradual extinguishment of generative potency.

Reactions of the female organs

The unfolding in a woman of the various phases of the sexual act is much the same as in a man, at least in the broad theoretical outline. In practice it is infinitely more complex. Three points must be underscored and recalled:

1. *The female orgasm can be attained only after a more or less extended period of sexual "habituation."* Normally and even quite usually it *does not take place* in early sexual relations and so a woman must not on that account be taxed with being frigid. The explanation is an easy one. For one thing, what is known about psychosexual development in a woman makes such a latency of the orgasm readily understandable in the light of the fact that very few women have any knowledge of the kind of sensations they are going to feel. And again, as has been stated before, a woman's genital apparatus has caused her, since puberty, nothing but discomfort and trouble. It takes some time for her to "go into reverse" and learn that her sexual system can be the source of pleasure and deep satisfaction.

2. *In a woman, preponderance is given to psychic stimuli in the activation of the processes that lead to orgasm.* This, too, has already been discussed at some length.

Let it simply be recalled that in a man sensuality outruns tenderness, while in a woman the reverse is true. No other preparation for sexual union can replace for her the emotional preliminaries. Without a favorable psychological climate, the physical conditions of a proper orgasm cannot be established.

3. *The sexual tempo of a woman is perceptibly slower than that of a man.* Hence the absolute necessity for a man to be self-disciplined, patient and ready to co-ordinate his pace with that of his wife, otherwise he will run the course to its end, complete enjoyment, while she lags far behind near the starting point.

A) *The tumescent phase.*

Following the period of preparation, the phase of tumescence proper begins with the penetration by the penis and lasts two to five minutes on the average.

Much has already been said on the capital importance of psychic stimulation through all manner of signals, messages, ideas and sentiments impregnated with sexual or emotional meaning. The five senses can also provide excitation, but none of them can do so with complete independence from emotional factors, even though the areas of erotic desire in a woman's body are spread far wider than similar zones in a man.

The two main areas of physical excitability in a woman are the clitoris and the labia minora. Because the female orgasm is rather long in coming, a preliminary excitation of the clitoris is often required. For some women this is the only moment of enjoyment, an incomplete pleasure to be sure, but one which is accepted as satisfactory for lack of anything better. For other women this step is use- less and even unpleasant. As for the orgasm which origi- nates in the vagina, it may have various degrees, but there is still much to be learned about the domain of such vaginal climaxes.

Just as it was observed in a man, the tumescent phase is marked in a woman by phenomena of genital congestion and swelling, increased glandular secretion, erection of the clitoris (whose role is essential to the proper harmony of intercourse), and hardening of the nipples.

All the stimuli activate the genital nerve centers which are located, as they are in man, at the base of the spine. They co-ordinate all the vasomotor and secretory processes which develop automatically and in succession, to end in the orgasm.

B) *The orgasm proper.*

In a woman,

> intercourse is never completely ended: it has no terminal point. The pleasure of the male rises like an arrow, and when it has reached a certain threshold it is fulfilled and dissolves into orgasm. The delight of the female radiates through the whole body, never remaining centered within the genital sys- tem alone. Even there, the contractions of the vagina, rather than being a real orgastic spasm, are more like rhythmic waves that build up, then flatten out, then surge again, crest- ing at times, then breaking once more and quieting, but never quite completely fading out. . . . (Simone de Beauvoir)

This welter of sensual delight is generally stirred by the sensing of the male's ejaculation of his semen. It is composed:

—of spasmodic neuro-muscular reactions of local as well as general organic nature; and

—of secretional reflexes affecting the accessory genital glands and the sudoriferous, or sweat-producing glands. For the female excitation is accompanied indeed by a real ejaculation from these accessory glandular centers.

—of circulatory and respiratory reactions similar to those described in the man.

If the man's ejaculation is premature, or if *coitus interruptus* is practiced, a woman will have difficulty reaching her climax.

C) *The final phase of detumescence.*

It is practically the same as in a man, characterized as it is by a relaxing of all nervous and muscular tension, a feeling of euphoria and drowsiness.

VI

Masturbation

Masturbation is defined as "the excitement of one's own genital organs by unnatural means," or again as "the consciously wanted and freely accepted exercise of the reproductive function for solitary satisfaction." The moment of its occurrence is one of total severance of all real emotional contact with other human beings.[1]

It is a dreadfully selfish passion which considerably narrows the horizons of one who indulges in it as a habit, since it only generates feelings of dejection, guilt and distress.

The study of masturbation must take into account not only the act itself, but also every one of the repercussions it has on mind and body.

THE PHYSICAL ASPECTS OF LOVE

The frequency of youthful self-abuse

It has been known for a very long time that few individuals are able to run, unhurt, the gauntlet of puberty. But it has taken our own statistics-minded era to introduce the element of exact figures into this previously diffuse and secretive area of knowledge. In America, Doctor Kinsey and his assistants have established, through extensive and long research, that from the start of the pubertal period onward at least 85 percent of all boys practice onanism; but it was also revealed that the vast majority, or 65 percent, spontaneously and permanently abandon the practice within four years' time.

Now, it must be made very clear that this nearly universal stage of masturbational conduct is not at all essential to the acquiring of adult maturity in sexuality. It is nonetheless true that the state of change in an adolescent's sexual instinct, his ignorance concerning woman, and his misconceptions about the realities of human sex all tend to make pubertal masturbation practically so unavoidable, except for pathological cases of sexual disinterest, that it must appear to be biologically normal and the object of neither amazement nor fear, despite its frequency.

The very close and sufficiently constant relation between masturbation and puberty quite naturally invites the conclusion that the practice is not due solely to chance, but to a certain number of factors which determine and promote it in this particular period of life.

Before defining the truly responsible factors, one must rule out the alleged and specious "overflow" factor. Those who argue for it forget the fact that a spontaneous evacuation of the genital reservoirs is provided for by night pollutions (the so-called "wet dreams"), as well as by the voiding mechanisms of the bladder and rectum. Actually it is quite frequent for masturbation to take place shortly after an unprovoked pollution.

What then are the real factors of masturbation?

A) At puberty, as was stated earlier, the personality of the adolescent has not yet asserted itself and is strangely open to any influence. His soul and mind at this time are like a jousting field of knighthood days where contradictory influences combat each other. The fundamental trait of the physiology and the psychology of pubertal age is *instability*.

The factors of this instability are:

1) The chaotic condition of the emotional frame, brought about by the coexistence within it, and the successive impacts, of contradictory feelings and impulses. The adolescent is fighting to become self-determinant, but his struggle meets constant opposition and threats. This explains why a boy this age is so often morose, depressed and anguished.

2) Emotional instability is conditioned by a corre-

sponding state of turmoil and changeableness in the functionings of glands and nerves. The conquest of adult balance in the dual psychic and physical realm is a slow and long achievement.

3) Will power is, of course, beginning to appear and assert itself, notably in the boy's effort to become independent. But because it is so absorbed in its own development, this strength of will does not have the sufficient energy left to ensure a satisfactory regulation of the adolescent's emotional life.

B) Now, just when the whole organism is in turmoil and unbalanced, and when will power has only just begun to be educated, the youthful complex of body and mind is assailed by new and extremely violent urges to which it can oppose no valid compensating force. The boy is biologically an adult, but he lacks the means of measuring up to the tasks and responsibilities of a man.

1) The potent surge of the sex hormones prompts the growth of the genital parts, and spurs the activity of the spermatic cells. Simultaneously, tension increases within the testes. Everything fosters the excitability of the genitals and gives the sex impulse greater strength. The sexual urge is all the stronger because, in the first stages of puberty at least, sexuality evolves much earlier and more quickly than does "erotic" life, taking this word to mean "normal physical love." In the absence of any clear concept of love, the youngster is delivered over to all the incitements of a *sexual instinct, as yet untempered by its eventual integration into the personality.*

2) Other stimulants concur in reinforcing sexuality. Imaginative fancies and reveries afford the pubescent child the chance to escape from reality and to withdraw within himself as he fondles in his mind the images born of newly awakened desires. Reality, thus veiled and muted, cannot offset fiction. It is inevitable therefore, in the condition of "pubertal rapture" for sexual excitation to reach such a pitch that by itself the door opens to sexual acts of the simplest and easiest kind. Of itself, day-dreaming eases the way to masturbation, since both activities set aside the discipline of reality and encourage the withdrawal within self, leaving one entirely open to the sway of gratification.

Masturbation and its results

A) *Physical consequences:* these are of quite minimal importance, as masturbation causes loss of muscle tone, pains in the region of the loins (back-pains in the areas extending from the lower ribs to the hip-bones), loss of appetite and sometimes sleep.

B) *Mental consequences:* these also are of minor importance, consisting in a lessening of attentiveness and memory.

C) *Sexual consequences:* these are more serious, because masturbation leads to the creation of conditioned reflexes.

Clinical experience of almost daily frequency reveals that a great number of men enter the marriage state handicapped with a long-established, and sometimes persisting habit of masturbation. At the most deeply subconscious level of instinctive life, it is evidence of "an uncompleted stage of instinctive sexual behavior which has remained self-centered, with all the more or less obsessional elements involved." This means that the subject still retains in himself "something like a subconscious, instinctive need for self-erotic compensation when he is face to face with certain difficulties of everyday existence." This, of course, has more or less deep repercussions on the harmony of the married couple, not only in the matter of sex relations, but also from the psychological and the spiritual point of view. It will also contribute, in more than just a slight degree, to making more difficult the already delicate task which two human beings face when they want to become adapted to each other.[2]

What are the emotional and moral consequences?

These are the most serious consequences of masturbation, since they entail a *mutilation of love*. In order to correctly gauge the significance of this elementary sexual act of masturbation one must use as a point of reference the real and true notion of human sexuality, which cannot be conceived outside the mutual love and faithfulness of a man and woman intimately joined in the unity of body, mind and emotions, and performing a creative act that involves the total gift of one's self to the other.

The act of masturbation is not just a single but a double shifting of the sexual act away from its purposeful end, first because it presupposes the absence of all emotional contact and responsible pledge, and secondly because it utterly nullifies the procreative intent of human love.

And so the deliberate pursuit of solitary sexual pleasure is a double evasion: a running away from the biological realities of the species, and a flight from the psycho-emotional facts of human sex. It is the exact opposite of the vision of love—responsible, enriching, growth-imparting love. It is "confinement within the ever shrinking bounds of a fear-struck, impoverishing and selfish gratification." Nothing is left of communication and fusion with another human being, but "the accent is placed on awareness of mere self," and the sexual act, bereft of its deep interior intent, expresses nothing more than emptiness.

In short, the great defect of masturbation and its gravest danger reside in what was called earlier the mutilation of love. "The whole symbolic significance of things corporeal in their relation to love is so narrowed down as to mean no more than a senseless sensation. The impossible is attempted: to have one's body and at the same time to be one's body." The result is a violent sundering, for it is now impossible to realize sexuality in its fullness, impossible also to attain love, which is essentially an *exchange* between *two* persons. The individual, psychically unsatisfied, goes on trying to fill his painful emotional void by repeating the act; masturbation calls for masturbation and soon becomes an inveterate, obsessive habit, a mechanical and compulsive act. All this leads to a moral and psychological crisis.

The individual usually feels that his behavior is abnormal, not in conformity with his true destiny, and that one of the most powerful, most explosive energies of his being is side-tracked and foiled. But, unable to rid himself of the habit, he comes to consider it as a *defect* which he is powerless to correct. He is incurable in his own eyes and becames entangled in a vicious circle. "The adolescent feels desire rise within him; he fights it down; he gives in." The depressed feeling which follows orgasm feeds on all his notions of guilt, sin and harmfulness; "he accuses himself, indulges in self-calumny, tries to stem the flood, to build up defense mechanisms; he wards off temptation at times, but at other times he comes to terms with it by granting himself a measure of satisfaction." The failure of will power becomes more accentuated, failing not with regard to self-abuse alone, but in all other matters also. An inferiority complex sets in, gravely compromising school achievement, and later social achievement, taming valid aggressiveness, quelling the spirit of enterprise and settling him in a state of semi-defeat.

His guilt complex becomes more and more distressing as the habit hedges him in more closely and he becomes more engrossed with himself to the point of dwelling in despairing solitude. Wrapped up in self-gratification, cut off from the world about him, living within his own world of fiction and absurdity, a world of phantasms with no outside vistas, he is soon the individual who exists in distressed isolation.

"The act of masturbation is really a symbol of defeat and helplessness of one who cannot love." It is a regression of personality back to the stage of infancy.

Ways of fighting the problem

"If we do not wish to see adolescents struggling with non-existent problems, flunking exams, dropping out of schools and careers, running away from themselves and their world, we must help them."

Yes indeed, but how? Masturbation will never yield to frontal attacks, and in any event a quick disappearance of the onanistic habit must not be expected. The following stumbling-blocks must be avoided:

A) One must not try explicitly to prevent masturbation *before* it sets in. This would be tantamount to provoking its appearance. Any intervention must be determined by factual knowledge that the adolescent does need help,

then guidance must be very prudent and extremely tactful.

B) One must not give exaggerated importance to commonplace instances of masturbation at the very beginning
of the pubertal period. To do so might jeopardize the
chances it has of disappearing by itself, and might open
the way to complications by making the practice obsessive.

Masturbation assumes several forms whose nature
must be explained to the adolescent; he must be made to
understand how certain acts that seem identical can really
be essentially different in the light of their purposive intent.

1. The first solitary acts are very often the results of
circumstances entirely beyond the control of will power;
their practice follows some spontaneous genital excitation,
or one that is provoked indirectly and *not wanted for
itself*. When masturbation takes this form, all one need
do is to arouse in the boy a desire to create for himself
some ideal whose influence will tend to clear the air about
him of eroticism. Some sensible advice is also called for
regarding general hygiene and food habits.

2. Failing this, the adolescent may quite soon begin to
seek erotic satisfactions in full awareness, and take up the
practice of *willful* masturbation, with sensuous delight as
his deliberate objective. He then acquiesces to these ventures in giving in to himself, in letting his person be bent
to a yoke; "the body is dissociated from the person, sexual

function from love which gives it meaning, the individual from the world about him." The moral problem is posed, as are the psychological and emotional perplexities. Little by little the young person falls under the tyranny of the habit. He is led to intensify the excitation, with the risk of perversions like sadism or masochism, unless he becomes openly narcissistic and derives sensual pleasure from the contemplation of his own body in the state of sexual excitation.

3. Finally there is the third type of case in which imagination, by conjuring up the picture of a partner of the opposite sex, makes masturbation assume the aspect of hetero-erotism. Some authorities in this field, among them Oswald Schwarz, view this form of masturbation as a transition to definitive sexuality. That is, the subject resorts to masturbation only as to a makeshift, while dwelling in his mind upon the ideal of normal intercourse of which self-abuse is an inkling. This, of course, reveals a lack of self-mastery, but at least it is not really sexual deviation. Under these conditions it is even preferable to recourse to the paid services of a prostitute, since "pathological human conduct always assumes more gravity when it affects a second party."

C) Fear and sense of guilt must *not* be called into play. Punishment, scolding, angry (and hypocritical) censure risk creating a maladjustment of balance which will later have adverse effects on the sexuality of the adult. Certainly this method can have lightning success, but only on the surface, because the urge to commit masturbation has not been resolved satisfactorily; it is merely repressed, sinks into the subconscious and permeates the psychological depths. This is the history of many a case of neurotic masturbatory fixation whose consequence is the reappearance later in life of this vice with renewed and brutal force.

* * *

The only valid way to proceed against masturbation consists in an attempt at regulation and readjustment, the direct opposite of repressive moves. A cure is obtained only by exploring the causes of the evil, by probing, with the adolescent, for the deep roots of his malady. He must be taught to practice extroversion, the natural attitude proper to his sex. He must be shown in what a vicious circle he has been turning. If this is done, progress will be sure and rapid.

Strong emphasis must be placed on the fact that masturbation, viewed in regard to adult personality, is *an immature form of sexual activity.* It is "unsocial," since it is neither oriented toward a partner of the other sex, nor directed toward the supra-individual purpose of sexuality, procreation. The adolescent must be made to see this form of sexuality as inferior, worthy only of his utter rejection if he wants to be what he so aspires to become, a man in every sense of the word. One of the best of preventive treatments for masturbation lies in orienting education, both in sex and in general, toward strengthening of will power and easing the integration of sexuality with the whole personality.

Fortunately many factors concur to assist the educator. Indeed at the very moment the adolescent is tending toward withdrawal in and upon himself, he also feels the need to project himself outwards. Morever he is discovering the world outside and the meaning of life; human values are revealing themselves to him; he is beginning to deal with abstract ideas; his artistic sense is awakening at the touch of education; he is stirred for the first time by religious or poetic emotions; he is learning about social relationships, their role, complexity and need. In the light of all this, his pubescent sexuality tends spontaneously to relax the tyrannical and restrictive hold it has upon him. His sexuality indeed moves into its rightful place in the scale of human values. If all these factors are properly reckoned with and every adolescent need is met, the boy will have all the help he needs to avoid becoming boxed in a negative attitude. Since he wants to become an adult and behave like one he has to be taught genuinely human and mature notions of sexuality. Such notions can and must constitute an ideal that will play in his life the part of a positive reality.

It was pointed out that frequent masturbation unavoidably brings on a feeling of anxiety. Part of the problem is to dispel this anxiety. Great care must be taken not to crush the "sinner" under reproaches that serve only to accentuate the guilt and inferiority complexes. Without appearing, naturally, to be giving even tacit approval to an act which is morally wrong and biologically abnormal, the counsellor must counteract the sense of guilt associated with masturbation by situating it in the general context of the young man's life.

This can be done by building up and praising the wholesome traits of the youth's personality, by restoring his confidence through self-respect and effort, and by calling into play the factors described just a moment ago.

But the educator, parent or counsellor, must go further. The anxiety mechanism must be deactivated. Anxiety is set in motion by the repression of emotional affectivity and by the dissociation of emotional life from sex life. Conflict arises between the need for human contacts that satisfy emotiveness, and the fear of things sexual. The educator's task will be to awaken the young man to heterosexual love and induce him to break out of the gloomy isolation by associating with other persons, particularly with young ladies. This kind of counselling is precisely what was called, in the early pages of this book, the education in love. *The adolescent needs directives that guide and comfort him, not just fences that block his approach to areas of danger.* The qualities of the female sex should be emphasized : a woman's beauty, for example, the nature of her emotional affectivity, her intuitive power, and the attitude she has towards life. The young man must be impressed with the necessity of his getting to know the soul of a young woman and the reality of his own sense of incompleteness which drives him in the needful, but always difficult, search for the other half of himself.

It must be remembered that none of this guidance will have any positive value or real efficacy unless the child, the adolescent or the young man remains throughout this period in rather close contact with the person who is advising him and supporting his individual effort. Such a postulate makes it abundantly clear that the persons pre-eminently suited to play this role in guidance and education are *the parents*.

Masturbation after puberty

Granting that pubertal masturbation is a biologically commonplace habit that will power may have difficulty in overcoming and eliminating, its persistence into adulthood is a much more serious matter. It may even become a frankly pathological problem when its continuance results from the definitive satisfaction it affords the subject. In these circumstances it is nearly always proof of some abnormality in emotion or character.

Individuals so constituted are generally afflicted with lowered vitality and neurasthenia. A person of this kind

> . . . is often the victim of an obsession; he is powerless to drive off the fantasies that assail him and endlessly occupy

181

his broody mental musings; he is always a falterer, a halfway man, spending his life in pro-and-con vacillation, wondering whether to act or not to act. Fated to failure or to half-success in every enterprise because of his lack of self-assurance, often jumped on by his relatives, feeling alone in a hostile, or at least uncomprehending world, this person of weak nerve and confused emotions has come upon self-abuse and has found its practice an outlet and a fleeting appeasement for his deep anxiety, for his permanent distress in the face of the difficult and strenuous problem of living. Masturbation becomes for him an imperative necessity that gives his nervous tension release and relief and also lulls the need of seeking and finding the normal way to exercise his sexuality. These "habituals" sometimes manage to achieve sexual balance in marriage, if they once decide for it; but it is not marriage that will cure the temperamental ailment which is at the root of their vice. The fact is that their psycho-neurasthenic disposition will respond only to a treatment compounded of personal or professional success, of integration and adequate utilization of their human potentialities.[3]

VII

Birth Control

Contraception or birth control?

Among human beings, as we have seen, the sexual urge tends to escape domination by the sex hormones. That is to say it is not, as in animals, a merely automatic response in terms of which sexual activity is tied in with the unique moment of readiness to fertilize. In mankind sexual activity is operable at all times, and conscious interest centers on sexual intercourse itself, not on fecundation. Therefore, the psychological aims of sexual relations between husband and wife—an essential factor in family and social stability—greatly overshadow the biological purpose of procreation.

While it is true that for thousands of years human fertility has been checked and balanced by natural forces

183

regulating and, to a degree, counterbalancing birth rate against death rate, these regulating mechanisms no longer function as they did. The results can be read in the sharply rising curve of birth rate which is seen as turning into a flood of overpopulation. Nearly every human home, and not just the very poor one, now is faced with this very grave and sometimes very distressing problem. Is it not desirable, in the current situation of living and housing conditions, that each married couple should be able to decide, on good and clear grounds, how many children there must be and at what intervals their births must occur? Could anyone blame a couple who would decide to have no more than three, four or five children?

Without regard here to the demographic aspects of the question, let it be stated that many reasons do make it desirable for a couple to limit the number of children and to space their birth at will.

Medical reasons: Among others, can be named heart disease, tuberculosis, nephritic hypertension and even quite simple concern for the well-being of a mother whose physical health is already impaired, or whose nerves are unstrung by earlier pregnancies and births with their train of worries and sleepless nights.

Reasons of proper housing: Current housing conditions all too often bring on situations of promiscuity which are as harmful in a moral sense as they are in terms of hygiene and comfort.

Economic reasons: The feeding, clothing, medical care,

etc., of children demand too often that the father work unrelentingly, and the mother perform miracles of ingenious and fatiguing resourcefulness in balancing an over-burdened budget.

Concern over education: These children must be given an education through the kind of instruction that will correspond to their tastes and their possibilities. They must not be forced to come down in the world even before they have started to grow up in it. Even the most hackneyed of truisms must be said again here: educating man's child is a longer, a more exacting and exhausting task than that of training a small animal.

The question of how many children it is desirable for each couple to have is thus a variable of many factors whose solution must rest with the interested parties; they and only they can settle the problem in the light of their religious or philosophical convictions and with due regard for their health, their fortune, and so on. And barring some exceptional cases, it is obvious that such a couple will not be able to limit sex relations solely to those required for the purpose of fertilization and pregnancy.

Here then is the problem of birth control, a crucial one for every couple. How shall this control be exercised? Shall it be through abortion, through Malthusian propaganda, or through a deliberate and fully conscious recognition that human beings have the capacity to limit births in ways that do not in the least impair their humanness? Between the well-intentioned but vague "be careful!"

attitude of some, and the ruthless methods of contraception, there is perhaps a middle-ground position which may reconcile the demands of morality with the requirements for a married life that is well-balanced and satisfying, and in which extended continence is neither possible nor desirable.

Many solutions have been proposed, and their worth will be discussed in a moment. Let it first be said that there seems to be little likelihood that, with respect to so delicate a problem, solutions will ever be found which will be valid for every person and in every case. That would not be in accord with the very laws of biology. Clarification and precise information about this subject must be all the more reasoned, all the more carefully weighed and all the more supported by valid argument as the practical problems of married couples daily become more acute. Far from having an easy solution, these questions are extremely complex in their settlement. One cannot allow himself to readily affirm or deny some point at issue, but must carefully ponder the various elements of decision.

Methods of preventing conception

Their general purpose is to prevent the meeting and fusion of the male and female generative cells without

interfering with the sensations inherent in sexual intercourse.

A) *Practices requiring no accessories*

Coitus interruptus, described in its Latin terms which
mean "interrupted intercourse," consists in the premature
withdrawal of the penis, causing the ejaculation to be
spent outside the woman's body. The effectiveness of this
process as a contraceptive is problematic, for one single
drop of semen deposited within the passages of the female
generative system might be enough for impregnation to
take place. It has other drawbacks: physically, since it
leaves the organs of the woman's lower pelvic area unre-
lieved of their congestion and tension and this soon leads
to chronic inflammation of the uterus and its subsidiary
organs; psychologically it breeds neuroses of varying intensity in the woman who is deprived of satisfaction and
cannot reach her climax. Finally it is condemned in the
Bible, and proscribed also by the Catholic Church.

Vulvar coitus, intercourse during which penetration
and ejaculation are not allowed to go beyond the vulva,
has the same drawbacks as coitus interruptus.

Coitus reservatus is the form of intercourse in which
copulation is complete and penetration deep, but ejaculation is withheld by the male partner by the exercise of
will power and psychological self-control. As a contraceptive method this is completely impossible for the majority of sexually normal men.

B) *Practices which require the use of devices*

1. *Mechanical devices:* for a man, these generally consist in coverings which enclose the penis, preventing the ejaculated semen from entering the passages of the woman's organs of reproduction. For a woman, they would be sponges, saturated or not with solutions that destroy the spermatozoa, or vaginal diaphragms of various kinds.

2. *Chemical devices:* these may range from irrigations (douches) with plain water, or light antiseptic solutions, to the use of vaginal suppositories, powders, jellies, or various combinations of these.

The very multiplicity of contraceptive methods and devices suggests that none of them is foolproof. However, if several are used simultaneously, a sufficiently high rate of success is assured. But setting aside the moral question, they are not without physical and psychological danger for a woman.

Physical trouble of a localized nature may be caused by the chemical preparations used. Some theories hold that even irrigation with plain cold water immediately after intercourse, with the chilling effect it has upon the still-congested organs, could possibly result in the inflammation of the womb (metritis) and of the Fallopian tubes (salpingitis). The different chemicals used as antiseptics may cause inflammation of the vagina (vaginitis) ; some of them may even have toxic effects upon the organism in general.

Symptoms of general organic disturbances may appear,

constituting what may be called the "cheating woman
syndrome." That these disturbances have their roots in
contraceptive practices in general, and in coitus interruptus in particular, is a fact of almost no doubt since they
are so often detected in women who practice contraception
or are subjected to it. When the congestion of the entire
genital zone, brought on by intercourse, is abruptly and
brutally deprived of its support before it comes to its
normal end, the neuro-vegetative system is thrown seriously out of balance. The symptoms of this appear [1] in
the lower areas of the pelvis and back; they consist in
feelings of heaviness in the lower abdomen, itching of the
vulva and the vagina, pains in the sacro-lumbar regions,
exaggeration, followed by dwindling of the menstrual
flow, metrorragia (flooding and hemorrhaging of the
uterus), vaginal inflammation, progressive sexual indifference, etc. Further disorders become detectable, some
of them of psychological order; digestive upsets, heat
flashes, anxiety, depression, phobias, and so forth.

Need it be repeated that contraceptive practices, in
whatever form, are dangerous? Yet that is not the whole
story.

Since none of the contraceptive devices or methods is a
sure means to the desired end, there always persists a feeling of worry, a fretfulness that proves disastrous to real
love. It might be added that the very use of different devices is of itself quite displeasing and vexing. For both
man and wife, the mutual gift of self is stripped of its inti-

mate and spontaneous quality, while in the wife herself the impression is born and grows that she is nothing more to her husband than a pleasure-giving machine.

The Ogino method

A) *Its principle*

It is a recognized fact that a woman cannot be impregnated at just any moment of the menstrual cycle. The life span of the ovum is no more than twenty-four hours, nor is that of the sperm beyond forty-eight hours. Fertilization is therefore possible during just a brief part of the cycle, around the moment of ovulation, *during the two or three days before ovulation, and from twenty-four to forty-eight hours after it.* This interval then sets apart two non-fertile periods, one occurring before the menstrual flow, the second after the end of the flow. Biology gives the assurance that there can be no fertilization in the course of these two periods. Intercourse may then take place without constraint of any kind, and can be normal in all respects, biological, anatomical and psychological. The question therefore of assuring or avoiding pregnancy resolves itself into fixing as accurately as possible the exact date of ovulation.

The Ogino method, also known as the "rhythm method," is based on these principles. Doctor Ogino conducted a statistical study of more than five hundred incidences of

190

ovulation. His stroke of genius consisted in perceiving that the date of ovulation has to be calculated *not* in regard to the *preceding* menstruation, but in regard to the *following* one. The ovulation date thus practically always occurs between the sixteenth and the twelfth day *before* menstruation.

These findings also revealed that the method could be difficult to follow, since its effectiveness rests on the ability to *foresee* an event yet to come. To use the Ogino method it is sufficient, but necessary, to know the date of the *coming* menses; this amounts to knowing the habitual duration of the menstrual cycle in a given woman. To find this out one studies the dates of the last twelve menstruations.

1. If the cycle is regular, of twenty-eight day duration, there is no difficulty: fertilization is possible, and continence is to be practiced, if pregnancy must be avoided, from the nineteenth to the twelfth day *before* the next menses.

2. If the cycle is not regular, being shorter or longer than the normal twenty-eight day cycle, it is slightly more difficult to calculate the time of possible fertility. This is how it must be done:

—the *beginning* of this time of possible fertilization is to be reckoned by *taking the shorter cycle,* subtracting *nineteen* from the total duration of this short cycle. For example, for a short twenty-six day cycle, the time of possible fertility will start seven days *from the beginning of the preceding menstruation.*

—the *end* of the time of possible fertility must be reckoned

191

by *taking the longer cycle,* subtracting *twelve* from the total duration of that cycle. For example, in a thirty-two day cycle, the time of possible fertility will *end* on the twentieth day *from the beginning of the preceding menses.*

B) *Objections and drawbacks to the Ogino method*

1. The Ogino method reduces the occasions of intercourse quite drastically, and this of course runs counter to the wishes of most couples, demanding as it does a capacity for austere self-restraint.

2. Its value is merely statistical. The ovulation date, far from being fixed and regular, can vary extremely as the cycle progresses. Ovulation is normally spontaneous but it may also be provoked and be either in advance of the normal time or after it, under the influence of such factors as climatic changes, illness, fatigue, emotional shocks, and even intercourse itself, not mentioning an extended life-span of the ova or the sperm.

3. No precise relation can be made between such independent phenomena as ovulation and menstruation. Some menstrual cycles seem normal and regular *without any ovulation,* while on the other hand the absence of periods does not strictly rule out the possibility of an ovulation and, consequently, the possibility of pregnancy. "There have been clinical observations to show beyond dispute that some women have become pregnant who had never had menstrual periods." (Palmer)

4. It must be noted finally that this method may not be practiced by Catholic couples without serious reasons that

dispense them, temporarily or definitively, from having a child, or if they have one or more, from having another. As Pope Pius XII said, "One may be dispensed from this positive, obligatory requirement for a long time, nay even for as long as marriage lasts, for serious reasons like those not uncommonly found and described as medical, eugenic, economical and social indications."

And so the Ogino method allows periodic practice of continence, but leaves a notably wide margin of doubt since it is valid in only sixty to seventy percent of the cases. There must therefore be found a more accurate procedure that might lower the rate of failure in controlling births under permissible conditions in terms of moral and religious belief. Such a procedure will now be discussed.

Determining the date of ovulation

A) *Procedures*

There are a certain number of ways to determine with sufficient precision the date of ovulation. Some are clinical signs and easy to observe: an isolated discharge of blood midway in the cycle; a spasm of pain in the lower abdomen; or a colorless, thin, clear mucous vaginal discharge. Other ways are by laboratory techniques: examination of vaginal smears; study of the cervical secretions; muscular tests; hormonal measurements, etc.

A procedure described as the method of "the temperature curve" [2] is one of the simplest and most reliable. It is based on the following data:

—During menstruation, temperatures usually are falling.

—During the first part of the menstrual cycle, from the fifth to the twelfth day, while the ovum is maturing the temperature is relatively low, about 97.5°F. (orally).

—Ovulation is often preceded by a low point in the temperatures. Then, after ovulation, the temperatures rise progressively for a few days to about 98.0°F.

—Finally, until the next menstruation, while luteal influence is dominant, temperature remains about 98.3°F. either steadily or with slight variations, until it drops again the day before or with menstruation.

These fluctuations in temperature are tied in with changes in hormonal dosage, as folliculine lowers temperature, and lutein causes it to rise. The temperature change on the fourteenth day reflects the reversal in hormonal predominance, the moment, namely, when the Graafian follicle (the ovisac) is transformed into the corpus luteum. All this is the sure sign that ovulation has just taken place, and temperature calls the signal.

This method, a very reliable one, demands only a minimum of elementary precautions which are, however, indispensable. The *same thermometer* must be used,[2] at the *same hour every day,* upon awakening and before rising; the temperature chart [3] must have a horizontal line for every tenth of a degree, and a vertical line for each day.

Finally, any factor likely to modify the temperature must be carefully noted on the chart: as a common cold, an infection or the disruption of the normal schedule of sleep.

B) *Conclusions on the method of the "temperature curve"*

The laboratory methods mentioned before and especially the "temperature curve" method tell that ovulation has taken place, *but in no way do they exactly predict its date.* Their value is, therefore, only in hindsight. For practical purposes, let it be said in summary of this method that:

1. Fertilization is possible only within the short interval between the moment of ovulation and the changing of the follicle into the corpus luteum. From this moment on, intercourse is bound to be fruitless.

2. As the average life span of a sperm cell is forty-eight hours within the female body, with some possible extension, any intercourse which takes place between menstruation and ovulation might result in pregnancy (if ovulation follows soon enough.)

3. In practical terms, that ovulation has taken place is proven by the rise of the temperature curve and the maintenance of a "high" phase. Intercourse must be ruled out until after this change (this in cases where a child is not desired).

Three objections of unequal value have been raised against this method. Each will be briefly stated and just as briefly answered.

Date	Readings and Notes	
	9 97 1 2 3 4 5 6 7 8 9 98 1 2 3 4 5 6 7 8 9 99 1	
	9 97 1 2 3 4 5 6 7 8 9 98 1 2 3 4 5 6 7 8 9 99 1	
	9 97 1 2 3 4 5 6 7 8 9 98 1 2 3 4 5 6 7 8 9 99 1	
	9 97 1 2 3 4 5 6 7 8 9 98 1 2 3 4 5 6 7 8 9 99 1	
	9 97 1 2 3 4 5 6 7 8 9 98 1 2 3 4 5 6 7 8 9 99 1	
	9 97 1 2 3 4 5 6 7 8 9 98 1 2 3 4 5 6 7 8 9 99 1	
	9 97 1 2 3 4 5 6 7 8 9 98 1 2 3 4 5 6 7 8 9 99 1	
	9 97 1 2 3 4 5 6 7 8 9 98 1 2 3 4 5 6 7 8 9 99 1	
	9 97 1 2 3 4 5 6 7 8 9 98 1 2 3 4 5 6 7 8 9 99 1	
	9 97 1 2 3 4 5 6 7 8 9 98 1 2 3 4 5 6 7 8 9 99 1	
	9 97 1 2 3 4 5 6 7 8 9 98 1 2 3 4 5 6 7 8 9 99 1	
	9 97 1 2 3 4 5 6 7 8 9 98 1 2 3 4 5 6 7 8 9 99 1	
	9 97 1 2 3 4 5 6 7 8 9 98 1 2 3 4 5 6 7 8 9 99 1	
	9 97 1 2 3 4 5 6 7 8 9 98 1 2 3 4 5 6 7 8 9 99 1	
	9 97 1 2 3 4 5 6 7 8 9 98 1 2 3 4 5 6 7 8 9 99 1	
	9 97 1 2 3 4 5 6 7 8 9 98 1 2 3 4 5 6 7 8 9 99 1	
	9 97 1 2 3 4 5 6 7 8 9 98 1 2 3 4 5 6 7 8 9 99 1	
	9 97 1 2 3 4 5 6 7 8 9 98 1 2 3 4 5 6 7 8 9 99 1	
	9 97 1 2 3 4 5 6 7 8 9 98 1 2 3 4 5 6 7 8 9 99 1	
	9 97 1 2 3 4 5 6 7 8 9 98 1 2 3 4 5 6 7 8 9 99 1	
	9 97 1 2 3 4 5 6 7 8 9 98 1 2 3 4 5 6 7 8 9 99 1	
	9 97 1 2 3 4 5 6 7 8 9 98 1 2 3 4 5 6 7 8 9 99 1	
	9 97 1 2 3 4 5 6 7 8 9 98 1 2 3 4 5 6 7 8 9 99 1	
	9 97 1 2 3 4 5 6 7 8 9 98 1 2 3 4 5 6 7 8 9 99 1	
	9 97 1 2 3 4 5 6 7 8 9 98 1 2 3 4 5 6 7 8 9 99 1	
	9 97 1 2 3 4 5 6 7 8 9 98 1 2 3 4 5 6 7 8 9 99 1	
	9 97 1 2 3 4 5 6 7 8 9 98 1 2 3 4 5 6 7 8 9 99 1	
	9 97 1 2 3 4 5 6 7 8 9 98 1 2 3 4 5 6 7 8 9 99 1	
	9 97 1 2 3 4 5 6 7 8 9 98 1 2 3 4 5 6 7 8 9 99 1	
	9 97 1 2 3 4 5 6 7 8 9 98 1 2 3 4 5 6 7 8 9 99 1	
	9 97 1 2 3 4 5 6 7 8 9 98 1 2 3 4 5 6 7 8 9 99 1	
	9 97 1 2 3 4 5 6 7 8 9 98 1 2 3 4 5 6 7 8 9 99 1	

97 98 99

little circle around the number corresponding to your temperature and make notes of signs. Your doctor will interpret your chart for you. To save his time, carefully read the handbook with the Ovulindex; it gives all the little details which will help you to use it successfully and answers common

and explains three typical temperature records. Fertility becomes more and more likely each day following the menses until the day when ovulation occurs. Fertility becomes less and less likely each day after ovulation. To increase or reduce the chance of conception, intercourse is timed accordingly.

Physicians may request copies of this chart without charge from:
Linacre Laboratories, Box 1938, New York 17, N.Y.

Ovulindex temperature chart

for use with the Ovulindex thermometer in determining the time and occurence of ovulation

Date	1960	Readings and Notes
10		9 97 1 2 3 4 5 6 7 8 9 98 1·2 3 4 5 6 7 8 9 99 1	27 28
11		9 97 1 2 3 4 5 6 7 8 9 98 1 2 3 4 5 6 7 8 9 99 1
12		9 97 1 2 3 4 5 6 7 8 9 98 1 2 3 4 5 6 7 8 M 99 1
13		9 97 1 2 3 4 5 6 7 8 9 98 1 2 3 4 5 6 7 8 M 99 1
14		9 97 1 2 3 4 5 6 7 8 9 98 1 2 3 4 5 6 7 8 M 99 1
15		9 97 1 2 3 4 5 6 7 8 9 98 1 2 3 4 5 6 7 8 M 99 1
16		9 97 1 2 3 4 5 6 7 8 C 98 1 2 3 4 5 6 7 8 9 99 1
17		9 97 1 2 3 4 5 6 7 8 C 98 1 2 3 4 5 6 7 8 9 99 1
18		9 97 1 2 3 4 5 6 7 8 9 98 1 2 3 4 5 6 7 8 9 99 1
19		9 97 1 2 3 4 5 6 7 8 9 9 1 *Slept late* 9 99 1
20		9 97 1 2 3 4 5 6 7 8 9 98 1 2 3 4 5 6 7 8 9 99 1
21		9 97 1 2 3 4 5 *7 mucus thick, slight*
22		9 97 1 2 3 4 *mucus clear* 6 7 8 9 99 1
23		9 97 1 2 3 4 *much mucus, thin* 1
24		9 97 1 2 3 4 *much mucus* 6 7 8 9 99 1 ~~PROBABLE OVULATION~~
25		9 97 1 2 3 4 5 6 *slight mucus* 99 1
26		9 97 1 2 3 4 5 6 7 8 9 98 1 2 3 4 5 6 7 8 9 99 1
27		9 97 1 2 3 4 5 6 7 8 9 98 1 2 3 4 5 6 7 8 9 99 1
28		9 97 1 2 3 4 5 6 7 8 9 98 1 2 3 C 5 6 7 8 9 99 1
29		9 97 1 2 3 4 5 6 7 8 9 98 1 2 3 4 5 6 7 8 9 99 1
30		9 97 1 2 3 4 5 6 7 8 9 98 1 2 3 4 5 6 7 8 9 99 1
/1		9 97 1 2 3 4 5 6 7 8 9 98 1 2 3 C 5 6 7 8 9 99 1
2		9 97 1 2 3 4 5 6 7 8 9 98 1 2 3 4 5 6 7 8 9 99 1
3		9 97 1 2 3 4 5 6 7 8 9 98 1 2 3 4 5 6 7 8 9 99 1
4		9 97 1 2 *forgot* 98 1 2 3 4 5 6 7 8 9 99 1
5		9 97 1 2 3 4 5 6 7 8 9 98 1 2 3 4 C 6 7 8 9 99 1
6		9 97 1 2 3 4 5 6 7 8 9 98 1 2 3 4 5 6 7 8 9 99 1
7		9 97 1 2 3 4 5 6 7 8 9 98 1 2 3 4 C 6 7 8 9 99 1
8		9 97 1 2 3 4 5 6 7 8 9 98 1 2 3 4 5 6 7 8 9 99 1
9		9 97 1 2 3 4 5 6 7 8 9 98 1 2 3 4 5 6 7 M 99 1
		9 97 1 2 3 4 5 6 7 8 9 98 1 2 3 4 5 6 7 8 9 99 1
		9 97 1 2 3 4 5 6 7 8 9 98 1 2 3 4 5 6 7 8 9 99 1
		9 97 1 2 3 4 5 6 7 8 9 98 1 2 3 4 5 6 7 8 9 99 1
		9 97 1 2 3 4 5 6 7 8 9 98 1 2 3 4 5 6 7 8 9 99 1

To obtain an Ovulindex thermometer, show this chart to your regular prescription druggist. He will have it in stock or will quickly get it for you from his wholesaler. Look for the name Ovulindex on the white kit-box and the enclosed 16-page handbook. Every Ovulindex is certified to register *within* 0.1° at *three* test points, 97°, 98° and 99°. Substitutes do not have this accuracy.

SPECIAL INSTRUCTIONS:

_____

_____

_____ M.D.

96   97   98   99   100

The Ovulindex thermometer

a) There might be several ovulations in the course of the one and same menstrual cycle. This possibility is ruled out by the best medical authorities.

b) Ovulation may take place without any rise in temperature. For one thing, this is generally in cases of sterility; for another, the absence of a temperature rise is the automatic signal that intercourse must not take place.

c) Certain temperature charts are difficult to interpret. This is true in rare cases which require that a physician be consulted to find the cause of these anomalies, and provide the proper treatment.

C) *Application of the "temperature curve" method to special post-natal cases*

1. *A woman who does not breast-feed:* menstruation usually begins again for her six weeks after delivery. But, in fifty percent of such cases, this resumed menstrual flow ends a cycle in which ovulation has occurred. This means that half the women who do not nurse their baby might become pregnant again before the first menstruation appears.

2. *A woman who does breast-feed:* only in exceptional cases does menstruation fail to start again before the third month after delivery; but the resumption of menstrual flow marks the end of an ovulation cycle *only* in seven percent of cases. This low percentage explains why pregnancy is so rare during breast-feeding, although its possibility is not at all ruled out.

3. The "temperature curve" method *can be effective* in

any case, provided intercourse is omitted as long as the temperatures are low.

*   *   *

The considerations of this second part of our study should have created the impression that both love and marriage do not evolve and mature by themselves. Happiness in marriage can mean happiness in love—and yet it must be remembered that success is only achieved through the sacrifice, patience, understanding and willingness of *both* partners.

Young Christians must face these facts and prepare themselves to deal with them by forming a truly Christian mentality toward love. As Monsignor Kelly points out in his *Introduction,* people must learn to see the beauty and vital importance of the Christian concept of sex. Only in this way will a marriage be on its way to success.

Certainly this volume is only a beginning to an education in love. For a further study of other aspects of Christian marriage, the reader should consult the list of recommended readings. It is hoped that the reader has gained an insight into, and a better knowledge of both the nature and function of love.

Notes and References

Foreword

1. Dr. Charles Rendu: "Le médecin dans la préparation au mariage," *Cahier Laënnec,* #2, 1955, p. 10.

Chapter One

1. See C. Koupernick: "Libres propos sur l'éducation sexuelle," *Concours médical,* #45, November 9, 1957, p. 4857.
2. C. Koupernick, *op. cit.*
3. Chanoine Bache, "Chasteté masculine," *Médecine et sexualité,* p. 123, Coll. Convergences, Ed. Spes.
4. See M. Bodènes, "L'évolution pubertaire," *Cahier Laënnec,* #1, 1955.

5. See Dr. Pauwels, "Psychisme et puberté," *Cahier Laënnec,* #1, 1955.
   6. *Ibid.*
   7. *Ibid.*
   8. Dr. Juliette Boutonnier, "La crise de la sexualité à la puberté," *Médecine et sexualité,* Coll. Convergences, Ed. Spes.
   9. *Ibid.*
   10. *Ibid.*
   11. *Ibid.*
   12. Dr. Pauwels, *op. cit.*
   13. On these various points, see Chapter II.
   14. Lettre aux éducateurs, *Puberté et problemes sexuels de l'adolescence,* p. 126, Centre d'études Laënnec, P. Lethielleux.
   15. See Paul Chauchard, *La Vie Sexuelle,* Coll. "Que sais-je?" P.U.F.
   16. G. Thibon, "La vie à deux," *Médecine et mariage,* Coll. Convergences, Ed. Spes.
   17. *Ibid.*
   18. P. Chauchard, *op. cit.,* p. 33.
   19. *Ibid.*
   20. Dr. Eck, *Bulletin de la Societé Saint-Luc,* #1, 1955, p. 10.
   21. Dr. Norman, *S'aimer corps et âme,* Ed. Casterman.
   22. P. Chauchard, *op. cit.,* pp. 91, 92.

Chapter Two

1. Dr. C. Rendu, *op. cit.*
   2. Dr. Vacher, *La psychologie sexuelle,* Grasset.
   3. G. Thibon, *op. cit.,* p. 254.
   4. Dr. Vacher, *op. cit.*
   5. *Ibid.*
   6. G. Thibon, *op. cit.*
   7. Dr. C. Rendu, *op. cit.,* pp. 15, 16.

8. Chanoine Barbe, "Aspects médico-psychologiques de la chasteté masculine dans le célibat et le mariage," *Médicine et sexualité,* p. 113, Coll. Convergences, Ed. Spes.

9. G. Thibon, *op. cit.,* p. 250.

10. Dr. Vacher, *op. cit.*

Chapter Three

1. See "Lettres aux éducateurs," *Puberté et problèmes sexuels de l'adolescence,* Centre d'études Laënnec, P. Lethielleux.

2. Dr. Gallimard, "Origine et traitement des hyper-activités sexuelles," *Médecine et sexualité,* pp. 164-165, Coll. Convergences, Ed. Spes.

3. *Translator's Note.* Don Juan is a hero of dramas by Tirso de Molina, Molière, Thomas Corneille, and Goldoni, of a ballet by Gluck, a poem by Byron, and an opera by Mozart. The original was Don Juan Tenorio of Seville, an aristocratic libertine of the fourteenth century. He is represented in the classic literary and operatic works of the authors cited above as aiming to seduce the daughter of the governor of Seville, or of a nobleman of the Ulloa family, but is then opposed by the father and kills him. Subsequently Don Juan visits the dead man's tomb, orders a feast to be prepared there, and invites the commemorative statue over the tomb to join him. The stone guest does so, but compels Don Juan to follow him and delivers him into the hands of the Devil.

4. G. Thibon, *op. cit.,* p. 247.

5. R. P. Riquet, *Bulletin de la Societé Saint-Luc,* #10, 1959.

6. *Ibid.*

7. Chanoine Lancremon, "Le célibat," *Médecine et mariage,* Coll. Convergences, Ed. Spes.

8. ———, "Le célibat, étude psycho-physiologique," *Médecine et mariage,* p. 58, Coll. Convergences, Ed. Spes.

9. J. Folliet, "Le célibat," *Semaine sociale de Bordeaux,* 1957, p. 268.

10. Dr. Eck, *Cahier Laënnec,* #4, 1956, p. 39.
11. Chanoine Lancremon, *op. cit.,* p. 58.

Chapter Five

1. Dr. P. Merle, "La biologie expérimentale de la sexualité," *Bulletin de la Societé Saint-Luc,* #4, 1954, p. 128.
2. Palazolli, *Les déficiences sexuelles chez l'homme,* Ed. Masson.
3. *Ibid.*

Chapter Six

1. In reference to the contents of this chapter, see *Puberté et problèmes sexuels de l'adolescence,* Centre d'études, Laënnec, P. Lethielleux.
2. See Marc Oraison, "Vie spirituelle, raison et instinct de reproduction," *Chronique sociale,* #4, 1957, p. 332.
3. Dr. Gallimard, "Les hyper-activités sexuelles," *Médecine et sexualité,* p. 167, Coll. Convergences, Ed. Spes.

Chapter Seven

1. *Editor's Note.* It should also be noted that this syndrome has been recorded in women who do not practice contraception and also in some who are not married. Excitation without orgasm has been said to be responsible.
2. The *Ovulindex* thermometer is accurate enough to permit a new one to replace one that might be broken.
3. See Dr. Chartier, "Fecondity et continence periodique," *Cahier Laënnec,* #4, 1954.

204

Further Readings
on Marriage

This list of recommended readings contains material on the general subject of marriage as both a sacrament and a way of life. It should provide the reader with informative and useful details on the many aspects of marriage.

Books

ALLERS, RUDOLPH and RAEMERS, SYDNEY. *Sex Psychology in Education*. St. Louis: Herder, 1937.

AYRINHAC, H. A. and LYDON, P. J. *Matrimonial Legislation in the New Code of Canon Law*. Revised edition; New York: Benziger Bros., 1938.

BALDWIN, VIRGINIA and LOUIS. *To Marry With Love*. Milwaukee: Bruce, 1958.

BANAHAN, JOHN S. *Instructions for Mixed Marriages*. Milwaukee: Bruce, 1957.

CAFFAREL, H. *Marriage Is Holy*. Chicago: Fides, 1957.

CARNEY, F. W. *The Purposes of Christian Marriage*. Washington, D. C.: Catholic University of America Press, 1950.

CLARK, WILLIAM R., O. P. *One in Mind, One in Heart, One in Affection*. Providence, R. I.: Providence College Press, 1952.

CLEMENS, ALPHONSE H. *Marriage and the Family*. New York: Prentice-Hall, 1957.

———, *Marriage and Family Relationships*. Washington, D. C.: Catholic University of America Press, 1950.

———, *Marriage Education and Counseling*. Washington, D. C.: Catholic University of America Press, 1951.

———, *The Cana Movement in the U.S*. Washington, D. C.: Catholic University of America Press, 1953.

CONWAY, J. D. *What They Ask About Marriage*. Chicago: Fides, 1950.

DE BLANC, IRVING and SCAVILLA, NORMA. *Sanctity and Success in Marriage*. Washington, D. C.: N. C. W. C. Family Life Bureau, 1956.

DOYLE, CHARLES H. *Cana Is Forever*. Garden City, N. Y.: Doubleday, 1958.

———, *Sins of Parents: Counsels on Marriage and Youth Guidance*. Tarrytown, N. Y.: The Nugent Press, 1951.

DUNN, H. E. *Self-Ideal of Selected Married Catholics*. Washington, D. C.: Catholic University of America Press, 1956.

FABREGUES, JEAN DE, *Christian Marriage*. New York: Hawthorn Books, 1959.

FILAS, FRANCIS L., S.J. *The Family for Families*. Chicago: Paluch Co., 1951.

FIRKEL, EVA. *Woman in the Modern World*. Chicago: Fides, 1956.

FOERSTER, F. W., M. D. *Marriage and the Sex Problem*. Philadelphia: Lippincott, 1936.

HEALY, EDWIN. *Marriage Guidance*. Chicago: Loyola University Press, 1948.

HOPE, WINGFIELD. *Life Together*. New York: Sheed and Ward, 1943.

206

IMBIORSKI, WALTER (ed.). *The New Cana Manual.* Chicago: Delaney 1957.

KANE, JOHN J. *Marriage and the Family.* New York: The Dryden Press, 1952.

————. *Together in Marriage.* Chicago: Fides, 1957.

KEENAN, ALAN, O. F. M., and RYAN, JOHN, M. D. *Marriage, a Medical and Sacramental Study.* New York: Sheed and Ward, 1955.

KELLY, AUDREY, M. D. *A Catholic Parents Guide to Sex Education.* New York: Hawthorn Books, 1962.

KELLY, MSGR. GEORGE A. *Birth Control and Catholics.* Garden City, N. Y.: Doubleday, 1963.

————. *The Catholic Marriage Manual.* New York: Random House, 1958.

KINSELLA, LEO J. *The Wife Desired.* Techny, Ill.: Divine Word Missionary Pub., 1953.

————. *The Man for Her.* Oak Park, Ill.: Valiant Publications, 1957.

KNOX, RONALD. *Bridegroom and Bride.* New York: Sheed and Ward, 1957.

LE CLERCQ, JACQUES. *Marriage, a Great Sacrament.* Dublin: Clonmore and Reynolds, 1951.

LORD, DANIEL A., S. J. *The Guidance of Parents.* St. Louis: The Queen's Work, 1944.

MAGNER, JAMES A. *The Art of Happy Marriage.* Milwaukee: Bruce, 1947.

McGRATH, M. E. *Role of the Catholic College in preparing for Marriage and Family Life.* Washington, D. C.: Catholic University of America Press, 1952.

MESSENGER, E. C. *Two in One Flesh.* Westminster: The Newman Press, 1950.

MIHANOVICH, CLEMENT S., SCHNEPP, GERALD J., S. M., and THOMAS, JOHN L., S. J. *A Guide to Catholic Marriage.* Milwaukee: Bruce, 1963.

MOORE, EDWARD. *The Case Against Birth Control.* New York: Century, 1931.

MURPHY, JOHN, M. D. and LAUX, JOHN D. *The Rhythm Way to Family Happiness*. New York: Hawthorn Books, 1960.

O'BRIEN, JOHN A. *Happy Marriage: Guidance Before and After*. Garden City, N. Y.: Hanover House, 1956.

PERKINS, MARY. *Beginning at Home*. Collegeville, Minn.: Liturgical Press, 1955.

REED, GRANTLY DICK, M. D. *Childbirth Without Fear*. New York: Harpers, 1944.

SATTLER, HENRY V. *Parents, Children and the Facts of Life*. Paterson, N. J.: St. Anthony Guild Press, 1952.

SCHMIEDLER, ERNST, O.S.B. *Marriage and the Family*. New York: McGraw-Hill, 1946.

SCHNEPP, GERALD J. and ALFRED. *To God Through Marriage*. Milwaukee: Bruce, 1958.

SHEED, FRANK J. *The Nullity of Marriage*. New York: Sheed and Ward, 1959.

————, *Society and Sanity*. New York: Sheed and Ward, 1953.

SHEEN, BISHOP FULTON J. *Three to Get Married*. New York: Sheed and Ward, 1951.

THIBON, GUSTAVE. *What God Has Joined Together*. Chicago: Henry Regnery Co., 1952.

THOMAS, JOHN L., S. J. *The American Catholic Family*. Englewood Cliffs, N. J.: Prentice-Hall, 1956.

————. *Marriage and Rhythm*. Westminster: The Newman Press, 1957.

TREVETT, R. F. *The Church and Sex*. New York: Hawthorn Books, 1960.

VON GAGERN, BARON FREDERICK, M. D. *The Meaning of Life and Marriage*. Translated from the German. Westminster: The Newman Press, 1954.

WARD, MAISIE (ed.). *Be Not Solicitous*. New York: Sheed and Ward, 1953.

WAYNE, J. G. *Morals and Marriage*. New York: Longmans Green, 1936.

WOODS, RALPH L. *The Catholic Concept of Love and Marriage*. Philadelphia: Lippincott, 1958.

Zimmerman, Carle C., and Cervantes, Lucius F., S. J. *Marriage and the Family*. Chicago: Regnery, 1956.

Pamphlets

MARRIAGE AS A VOCATION

Connell, Francis J., C. SS. R. *Marriage—Human or Divine?* New York: The Paulist Press. 10 cents.

Cox, Rev. Ignatius W., S. J. *The Divine Romance of Marriage*. New York: The Paulist Press. 10 cents.

McCown, J. H., S. J. *Man, Woman and God*. St. Louis, Mo.: The Queen's Work. 10 cents.

Noll, Bishop John F. *Seven Instructions Before Marriage*. Huntington, Ind.: Our Sunday Visitor Press. 30 cents.

O'Brien, John A. *Marriage a Vocation*. Notre Dame, Ind.: Ave Maria Press. 10 cents.

Pius XI, Pope. *Encyclical Letter on Christian Marriage* (*Casti Connubii*). New York: America Press, 1936. 25 cents.

Power, Richard E. *Marriage in Christ: the Rite of Marriage*. Collegeville, Minn.: The Liturgical Press. 10 cents.

Vann, Gerald, O. P. *Christian Married Love*. Collegeville, Minn.: The Liturgical Press. 10 cents.

EDUCATION IN LOVE

Hynes, Emerson. *Seven Keys to a Christian Home*. Washington, D. C.: National Catholic Welfare Conference. 25 cents.

Lovasik, Lawrence, G., S. V. D. *Making Marriage Click*. St. Paul, Minn.: Radio Replies Press. 15 cents.

Miller, Donald F., C. SS. R. *How to Be a Good Husband*. Ligouri, Mo.: Ligourian Pamphlet Office. 5 cents.

———. *How to Be a Good Wife*. Ligouri, Mo.: Ligourian Pamphlet Office. 5 cents.

O'BRIEN, JOHN A. *Ideal Marriage: How to Achieve It.* New York: The Paulist Press. 10 cents.

THE CATHOLIC MEDICAL VIEWPOINT

CONWAY, MSGR. J. D. *What They Ask About Marriage.* Notre Dame, Ind.: Ave Maria Press. 10 cents.

DOLAN, ALBERT H. *All the Answers About Marriage and Birth Control.* Chicago: Carmelite Press. 15 cents.

MEYER, FULGENCE, O. F. M. *Plain Talks on Marriage.* Cincinnati, Ohio: St. Francis Book Shop. 40 cents.

PIUS XII, POPE. *Moral Questions Affecting Married Life.* Washington, D. C.: National Catholic Welfare Conference. 20 cents.

SHEED, F. J. *Marriage and the Family.* New York: Sheed and Ward. 75 cents.

THOMAS, JOHN L., S. J. *Beginning Your Marriage.* Oak Park, Ill.: Delaney, 1956. 50 cents.

VANN, GERALD, O. P. *Christian Married Love.* Collegeville, Minn.: The Liturgical Press. 10 cents.

BIRTH CONTROL AND THE RHYTHM METHOD

CAWLEY, THOMAS. *Letter to an Unborn Child and His Answer.* Scranton, Penn.: Catholic Light Publishing Co. 5 cents.

CONWAY, MSGR. J. D. *What They Ask About Birth Control.* Notre Dame, Ind.: Ave Maria Press. 10 cents.

———. *What They Ask About the Rhythm.* Notre Dame, Ind.: Ave Maria Press. 10 cents.

LORD, DANIEL A., S. J. *A Mother Looks at Birth Control.* St. Louis: The Queen's Work. 10 cents.

MILLER, DONALD F., C. SS. R. *For Wives and Husbands Only.* Ligouri, Mo.: Ligourian Pamphlet Office. 25 cents.

———. *What's Your Reason for Birth Control?* Liguori, Mo.: Liguorian Pamphlet Office. 5 cents.

210

P IUS XII, P OPE. *Moral Questions Affecting Married Life.* Washington,
D. C.: National Catholic Welfare Conference. 20 cents.
Planned Parenthood: An Answer. Washington, D. C.: National Catho-
lic Welfare Conference. 10 cents.
R YAN, J OHN, M.D. *Family Limitation.* New York: Sheed and Ward.
50 cents.

AVOIDING DANGER AREAS IN MARRIAGE

H AUNGS, E DWIN C., S. J. *An Examination of Conscience for Married
Couples.* St. Louis, Mo.: The Queen's Work. 10 cents.
L OVER, J AMES F., C. SS. R. *Is Your Marriage on the Rocks?* New York:
The Paulist Press. 10 cents.
M ILLER, D ONALD F., C. SS. R. *How to Check Your Anger.* Liguori,
Mo.: Ligourian Pamphlet Office. 10 cents.
O'B RIEN, J OHN A. *Why Marriages Fail.* Notre Dame, Ind.: Ave Maria
Press. 10 cents.

MONEY AND MARRIAGE

C ORLEY, F RANCIS J. *Family Allowances,* St. Louis, Mo.: Institute of
Social Order. 12 cents.
D UNN, M ARGARET M. *Careers Do Not Make the Woman.* Washing-
ton, D. C.: National Catholic Welfare Conference. 5 cents.
L ORD, D ANIEL A., S. J. *Money Runs or Ruins the Home.* St. Louis,
Mo.: The Queen's Work. 10 cents.
S ENSER, B OB. *Should Wives Work?* Notre Dame, Ind.: Ave Maria
Press. 10 cents.

DIVORCE AND SEPARATION

C ONWAY, M SGR. J. D. *What They Ask About Divorce.* Notre Dame,
Ind.: Ave Maria Press. 10 cents.
———. *What They Ask About Marriage Cases.* Notre Dame, Ind.:
Ave Maria Press. 10 cents.

LORD, DANIEL, A., S. J. *About Divorce*. St. Louis: The Queen's Work, 1946. 10 cents.

MILLER, DONALD F., C. SS. R. *When May Husband and Wife Separate?* Ligouri, Mo.: Ligourian Pamphlet Office. 10 cents.

O'BRIEN, JOHN A. *Why Not Get a Divorce?* New York: The Paulist Press. 10 cents.

THE MIXED MARRIAGE

CARROL, THOMAS. *Mixing Your Marriage*. Collegeville, Minn.: Liturgical Press. 5 cents.

CONWAY, MSGR. J. D. *What They Ask About Mixed Marriages*. Notre Dame, Ind.: Ave Maria Press. 10 cents.

LILLY, WARREN, S. J. *The Mixed Marriage Prenuptial Contract*. New York: The Catholic Information Society. 5 cents.

MILLER, DONALD F., C. SS. R. *Program for Catholics in a Mixed Marriage*. Ligouri, Mo.: Ligourian Pamphlet Office. 10 cents.

RUMBLE AND CARTY, FATHERS. *Six Pre-Marriage Instructions for Catholics and Non-Catholics*. St. Paul, Minn.: Radio Replies Press. 15 cents.

THE CHOICE OF PARENTHOOD

ARNOLD, OREN. *Love Enough to Go Around*. Reprinted from *Better Homes and Gardens*. Notre Dame, Ind.: Ave Maria Press. 10 cents.

D'ORSONNENS, J. I., S. J. *Choosing Your Career!* New York: The Paulist Press. 10 cents.

Father, the Head of the Home. Washington, D. C.: National Catholic Welfare Conference. $1.50.

GANSS, GEORGE E., S. J. *On Thinking Out Vocations to Four States of Life*. St. Louis, Mo.: The Queen's Work. 10 cents.

KELLY, GERALD L. *Modern Youth and Chastity*. St. Louis: The Queen's Work, 1941. 25 cents.

KIRSCH, FELIX M., O. M. Cap. *The Sex Problem: A Challenge and an Opportunity*. New York: The Paulist Press. 10 cents.

KRIEGER, B. J. *How to Recognize a Vocation*. Ligouri, Mo.: Ligourian
Pamphlet Office. 10 cents.

LORD, DANIEL A., S. J. *Questions People Ask About Their Children*.
St. Louis: The Queen's Work. 25 cents.

MILLER, DONALD F., C. SS. R., *How to Be a Good Father*. Ligouri,
Mo.: Ligourian Pamphlet Office. 5 cents.

————. *Questions Parents Ask About Raising Children*. Ligouri, Mo.:
Ligourian Pamphlet Office. 25 cents.

The Parent-Educator Series in five volumes: "Parental Responsibility,"
"Teaching Prayer in the Home," "Teaching Obedience in the
Home," "Teaching Honesty in the Home" and "Teaching Citizen-
ship in the Home." Washington, D. C.: The Confraternity of
Christian Doctrine. 20 cents each.

SCHMIEDELER, EDGAR, O. S. B. *Parent and Child*. New York: The
Paulist Press. 10 cents.

————. *Your Child's World*. New York: The Paulist Press. 50 cents.

————. *Your Home: A Church in Miniature*. Washington, D. C.:
National Catholic Welfare Conference. 25 cents.

Towards a Better Family Life. Washington, D. C.: National Catholic
Welfare Conference. 35 cents.

RELIGION AND THE FAMILY

BRODERICK, MSGR. EDWIN B. *TV and Your Child*. New York: The
Paulist Press. 15 cents.

BUSCH, WILLIAM. *Family Prayers*. Collegeville, Minn.: The Liturgical
Press. 5 cents.

BYLES, KATHERINE DELMONICO. *Religion in the Home for Elementary
School Children*. New York: The Paulist Press. 15 cents.

————. *Religion in the Home for the Pre-School Child*. New York:
The Paulist Press. 15 cents.

FARRELL, JOHN and EILEEN. *This Is Cana*. St. Meinrad, Ind.: The
Grail. 10 cents.

For Happier Families. Chicago, Ill.: Coordinating Committee of the
Christian Family Movement. 75 cents.

McLoughlin, Helen. *Family Advent Customs.* Collegeville, Minn.: The Liturgical Press. 15 cents.

Mueller, Theresa. *Family Life in Christ.* Collegeville, Minn.: The Liturgical Press. 20 cents.

Stokes, Bernward, O. F. M. *How to Make Your House a Home.* Washington, D. C.: National Catholic Welfare Conference. 50 cents.

Weiser, Francis X., S. J. *Religious Customs in the Family.* Collegeville, Minn.: The Liturgical Press. 25 cents.

Index

Birth control, 110, 183-195
changes in attitudes, 12-13
continence, 110
contraception or, 111, 183-186
economic reasons, 184-185
educational reasons, 185-186
family limitation, 14, 15, 184-185
medical reasons, 184
method of preventing conception, 186-190
Ogino method, 190-193
rhythm method, 190-193
spacing births, 114, 184
use of self-control, 114
Bodènes, M., 34
Boutonnier, Dr. Juliett, 39, 40, 41, 42
Boys
behavior toward girls, 56
developing self-mastery, 55
masturbation, 48, 50
physical development, 34-35, 43-45, 49
respect for womanhood, 50, 75
sex education, 49-50
sexual development, 32, 44, 49
Brain, 58-65
control of sex behavior, 59-62
development of, 58-59
sexual pleasures and, 59-65
Breast-feeding, 198

Celibacy, 102
Chartier, Dr., 194

Chastity, 73, 113-124
continence and, 101-108, 117-120
in marriage, 108-113, 118-124
mastery over instinct, 108
practice of, 122-124
spiritual significance, 124-125
Chauchard, Dr. Paul, 58, 59
Children
answering questions of, 32-33, 51, 54
education of, 114, 185-186
sex education, 30-32, 46-49
sexual development, 30-31
Christian views of sex, 9-10, 13-14, 199
Climax, sexual, 90-94, 151, 155
female, 55, 91-93, 164-165
Clitoris, 45, 141, 143, 163-164
Coitus interruptus, 187
Compatibility, 76
Conjugal relations, 15, 69-98
concern for wife's feelings, 94-96
copulation, 159-161
first act, 76-80
intervals of continence, 115
mutual gift of self, 23-24, 97-98
reactions of female organs, 162-165
reactions of male organs, 156-162
Continence, 101-108
awareness of carnal desire, 116-123
before marriage, 102-103

Palmer, 192
Parents, 58-75
  role of, 180-181
  sex education given by, 11, 50-
    54, 75
Partners, 61-71
  choices of, 61-63
  personality of, 63-64
  search for a mate, 65-71
Pauwels, Dr., 35, 36, 37
Penis, 45, 137-138, 157-158
Personality, sex instinct and, 20
Physical aspects of love, 125-195
  birth control, 183-195
  masturbation, 167-182
  sex and human anatomy, 135-
    165
Pituitary gland, 144, 146, 148
Pleasure, sexual, 57, 62
  brain and, 59-65
  understanding, 127-131
Polygamy, 106-107
Pope Pius XII, 193
Population explosion, 184
Progesterone, 45-46, 140, 147
Promiscuity, sexual, 13
Prostate glands, 137
Prostitution, 103-105
Protestant Puritans view of sex,
  10, 12
Psychological aspects of love, 29-
  131
  continence and chastity, 101-126
  education in love, 29-73
  pleasures of sex, 127-131
  sexual harmony, 75-99

Puberty, 34-35
  growth of sex instincts, 35-37
  masturbation, 167-181
  physical characteristics, 42-46
  sex characteristics, 34, 43-44,
    135-136

Rendu, Dr. C., 23, 76, 91
Repressions, 116-118, 122, 125
Reproduction, 23, 69, 141-143
Respect and love, 74, 75
Rhythm method, 190-193
Riquet, R. P., 112, 119-120

Sartre, Jean-Paul, 68
Schwarz, Oswald, 177
Self-restraint, 11, 12, 108-109
Semen, 137-138, 144
Seminal vesicles, 136
Sensory reactions, 61-62, 151-153
Sex, 20-25
Sex education, 15, 50-57, 118-120
  adolescents, 56-57
  aim of, 101
  answering questions of children,
    51-52
  approaches, 48-50
  example of parents, 58-75
  for boys, 46-50
  for girls, 47-49, 52, 54
  given by parents, 50-54, 58, 75
  importance of, 24-25, 29
  time for, 46-49
  who should give, 50-56
Sex instinct, 20, 60-61, 151
  growth of, 35-37

220

The Author and His Book

DOCTOR HENRI GIBERT *was born in 1920 in Lezignon-Corbiere (Aude), France. He married the former Renée Moretti in 1944 while attending the Montpellier School of Medicine. Here his doctoral thesis was accepted and he received his degree in 1945. His subsequent work and study resulted in a degree from Marseilles, and the prized Bronze Medal of the Academy of Medicine. During the Second World War, he participated as a doctor in the Armed Forces, holding the rank of captain. Formerly he served as a staff doctor at the Montpellier Hospital and presently he is a specialist in homeopathy as well as being a medical expert for the law courts of France. In addition, he has been appointed as the Medical Inspector for the Department of Sports and is the Head Doctor for* Medico-Social Interbancaire *of Avignon. His other positions include his membership in the French National Syndicate of Homeopathic Physicians, the Vice-Presidency of the* Caisse d'Allocations Familialer de Vaucluse, *his office as counsellor for the city of Avignon and his participation in the Cultural Center of Avignon of which he was the founder. Dr. Gibert resides in Avignon with his wife and three children. His previous writings include numerous articles of both medical and popular interest for a variety of French journals and magazines.*

LOVE IN MARRIAGE *(Hawthorn, 1964) was set in type by the Sweetman Typesetting Corporation in New York City and was printed and bound by The Book Press, Brattleboro, Vermont. The body type was set on the Linotype in Caslon, reflecting the design of William Caslon who modelled his work on the Dutch types of the late seventeenth century.*

A HAWTHORN BOOK